G000270824

ARABIAN
EXODUS

ARABIAN EXODUS

Margaret Greely

J A ALLEN
London

ISBN 0 85131 223 3

Published in 1975 by J. A. Allen & Company Limited,
1 Lower Grosvenor Place, Buckingham Palace Road,
London, SW1W 0EL.

Design by Bill Ireson

Filmset in 11/13pt Monophoto Ehrhardt by
BAS Printers Limited, Wallop, Hampshire
Printed photolitho in Great Britain
by Ebenezer Baylis and Son Limited
The Trinity Press, Worcester, and London

Contents

List of Illustrations

Foreword

WHEN I first met the author of this book, the circulation of *Arab Horse News*, which she has edited with distinction for several years, was some 500 to 600. It is now in excess of 3,000 and its actual readership is much larger than that. This is some measure of the sympathetic interest shown in the Arabian horse, during the past 25 years.

Today, preservation of fauna is much to the fore. But just what is it to be preserved from? Plainly, in this instance, not extinction. The Arabian horse is not a candidate for the kind offices of the Rare Breeds Survival trust. The peril in which the breed might stand is rather that of bastardization, of losing its identity; not exactly a fate worse than death, but a close approximation. I do not mean, the crude form of bastardization, the introduction of alien blood in order to produce some momentarily fashionable speciality. The danger is rather that of making, from within the breed, the wrong selection: and the more widely diffused ownership and breeding of Arabian horses becomes, the greater the risk of this happening. See what the author says, in the context of the enormous inflation of numbers in the United States. Fashion has ever been the most baneful influence on horse breeding, often jeopardizing the very capacity for survival. And Americans are the most fashion-prone of people. Not that one wishes to single them out. There are countries in which wrong turnings have been taken, nor is it possible to say in the light of present evidence whether British breeders are on the right track. The breeder of Arabians is of necessity forced into a conservative attitude. At least as regards the end in view, though he may be liberal as regards the means. State Stud managers in Eastern Europe are no exception. One can hear them, Party members all, express opinions of such a traditionalist nature as would curdle the blood of Marx.

It is the core of the author's belief that the Blunts, almost a century ago, accepted the Bedouin's own definition of what constituted the authentic *asil* type, and his belief that horses of a certain ancestry were inevitably, infallibly and indelibly marked by external characteristics that excluded all possibility of doubt and error. In the light of this definition they made the correct selection, and after their expeditions to the Nejd and the borders of Irak they only added to their Stud animals which satisfied these criteria. The stock derived from this foundation has been disseminated over four continents, and continues today. Whilst this book was being written, two associations of Arabian breeders have formed in France.

One is committed to importation of British and Polish breeding stock, and standing at the State Stud at Pompadour is the stallion Baj, a great grandson of Skowronek. This book devotes much space to Skowronek and his origins, by way of proving that Lady Wentworth was justified in her assessment of his external characteristics, and her faith in the purity of his breeding.

Elsewhere the author shows that 'national' differences are bound to arise, if only because the criteria of selection within the breed varies from country to country. In Russia, for example, selection is determined by performance tests, including races. This is a substitute, in a mild form, for the method practised by the Bedouin, and not considered by them as worth stressing to outsiders. It applied less to the stallions than to the mares, since only the latter were ridden in war. We may regard the qualifying tests of youngsters under certain State run breeding systems as pale imitations of the *ghazu*. But in another respect there are consequences of the Arabian's change of mastership from Bedouin to Western hands which are as much psychological as physical, and arise out of the difference between Moslem and 'Frankish' society. In the world of the black tents, male-dominated as it was, women played a limited part in the life of the horse. True, they fed them, but they did not ride them (they rode camels) or attend any mating or birth, as did the men. But in Western countries a very high percentage of women own, or are involved in management, caring and riding of Arabian horses, constituting an influence, measurable but so far unmeasured.

Well, what difference has it made? Part of the answer can doubtless be found by contemplating the author's Well House Stud of Arabians at Brede in Sussex, which with characteristic modesty she hardly mentions in this book, of which I wish the reader much enjoyment.

ANTHONY DENT. *February 1975*   *St. Pierre-de-Chignac, Dordogne*

. . . . and yet it is not to be denyed,
but almost all the horsemen and breeders within
this kingdome doe much insist herein, so as if
a Neapolitan, Arabian, Barbarie or such like
bee brought into England, how inestimable
he is valued, prised and solde, and how all men
desire him, who can doubt?

NICHOLAS MORGAN OF CROLANE, IN KENT
Perfection of Horsemanship, 1609.

PART 1

Chapter I

Tradition and History

THE UNKNOWN poet-author of the Book of Job, written about 600 years before Solomon, over 2,000 years before Mahomet, and 1,500 years before Christ, thus describes what his eyes must often have witnessed:

Hast Thou given the horse strength? Hast Thou clothed his neck with thunder?
Cans't Thou make him afraid as a grasshopper? The glory of his nostrils is terrible.
He paweth in the valley, and rejoiceth in his strength; he goeth on to meet the armed
*   men.*
He mocketh at fear, and is not affrighted; neither turneth he back from the sword.
The quiver rattleth against him, the glittering spear and the shield.
He swalloweth the ground with fierceness and rage; neither believeth he that it is the
*   sound of the trumpet.*
He saith among the trumpets, Ha, ha, and he smelleth the battle afar, the thunder of
*   the captains and the shouting.*

The writer of this prose-poem is describing, not the nomad horsemen, the Sabaeans* and Chaldeans, on their war raids, which Job, the prosperous herdsman and his tribe had cause to fear, but rather the army of war chariots, and foot soldiers that accompanied some Hittite king on his way to conquest – or some Egyptian Pharaoh returning victorious. The land of Uz, where Job dwelt, was on the great caravan route that linked Syria with the Arabian peninsula, and somewhere in the region between Northern Egypt and the Euphrates where the history of civilization begins, lived this ancient breed of horse we know as the Arabian.

Many theories have been put forward as to the original home of the Arabian horse, and equally controversial theories regarding his descent. The sifting of evidence by the light of modern Science seems to rule out the theory that the Arabian horse originated solely in Arabia, his appearance there as a *ridden* horse, never driven, is of a later period than the existing records of his use both ridden, and driven in war chariots in Egypt and Syria. Upton, in *Gleanings from the Desert of Arabia* suggests that the boundaries of the original habitat of this horse of the desert were wider than is generally supposed:

The name of Arabia is said to have been derived from Arabah, Arabah lay between the mountains and the Red Sea. From Arabah the whole peninsula of

* Sabaeans. The ancient people of Yemen, in south-western Arabia. From Arabic Saba, or Sheba, which was said to be the capital.

the Arabs was called Arabia, and the people acquired the name of Arabs. Aram and the land of Uz were probably the names given to the two earliest divisions of the whole peninsula – Aram to Syria, and the Land of Uz to the rest of the peninsula, or perhaps, excluding the deserts, to the habitable parts thereof.

Lady Wentworth in *Thoroughbred Racing Stock*, has written the finest and most comprehensive chapters on the subject of the original and distribution of the true Arabian, and sums up the matter thus:

The more the Semitic horse line is studied, the more certain it appears that the wild horses of Central Arabia must have been closely akin to those of Syria, North Arabia and Chaldea, which formed a continuous country till they were gradually cut off from each other by those terrific volcanic disturbances to which the Harra bears witness, and by the ever progressive aridity with which Arabia is cursed.

With reference to the modern controversy regarding the origin of the authentic Arabian. The *derivatives* of the Arab would appear to have been claimed as the *progenitor* of the pure stock; a mistake easily made when one considers how soon ill-breeding and adverse conditions can change the conformation of a horse.

The opinion of Anthony Dent is worth recording. Quoting J. A. H. Potraz, he writes:

Potraz has traced the whole history of domestication of the horse in the Old World and its introduction into the Near East, with the parallel history of the roundabout road whereby a means of harnessing and guiding it was devised. He demonstrates that it was indeed a long way round, beginning with the harnessing of the ox to the plough, and the problem of how to steer it from the rear. All possible adaptations of the ox-yoke principle had inherent weaknesses when adapted to the horse, and in fact maximum efficiency in the harnessing of horses was not achieved by the time the last book of the Bible had been written, neither had the ultimate in the perfection of the saddle – the introduction of stirrups – dawned on the world. On the other hand he shows that the last really significant innovation in the design of bridles – the curb chain – had by then become a reality. At least one puzzling contradiction is explained: that between traveller's accounts of Arab horses ridden in halters and hackamores and working almost entirely by voice, and the equally valid evidence of the savagely severe oriental curb. Neither is 'original' to Arabia, and both systems have existed side by side throughout the Old World for the last twenty centuries or more. Potraz demonstrates that the arts of horsemanship and studsmanship in the countries surrounding Arabia have a great bearing on the origin and development of the

Arab horse, especially the splendid series of Assyrian reliefs, many of which are to be seen in the British Museum and show a horse with many characteristic 'Arabian' features, but on the whole much larger than the desert-bred Arab. Potraz maintains that Bedouin horse-breeding was founded on the ruins of the horse-breeding, primarily for war and secondarily for hunting, of the crescent of military Empires from Persia to Egypt, that flourished and died in the thirty centuries before the birth of Christ. All, except the Persians, worked from a basis of imported stock, since there was no indigenous wild stock in any of them. An interesting speculation made (perhaps inspired by a comparison of the massive, tall, hand-fed, artificially-watered Assyrian horse with the desert-bred Arab), that Bedouin horsemanship and horse-breeding may have had much in common with the Red Indian counterpart, since the comparison of the Western Mustang with the Andalusian warhorse from which it derives brings out much the same points; not only a dwarfing back towards the original size of the truly wild primeval horse of about 13 hands high, but also what I can only describe as 'desiccation' affecting not only size but conformation of the limbs and the

Seti I fighting against the Asiatics (circa 1370 B.C.). Seti I, the first king of the 19th dynasty, waged many wars in Syria and Palestine, and especially against the Hittites. His chief aim was to capture the city of Kadesh, the Hittite stronghold in the valley of the Orontes. He is seen here in his chariot with his favourite pair of horses named 'Great with Victory', upon a campaign described as 'the going up of Pharaoh to conquer the land of Kadesh'.

head. A certain hard fineness that is the product of untold privations. To put it bluntly, Potraz (and one should remark in passing that he has the right background for a practical author on horses, being the scion of a Prussian landowning family) does not believe, like myself, that the first horses came into Arab hands through the raiding by night of the picket-lines of chariot-borne expeditionary forces from the great empires on the perimeter of Arabia, but thinks that they were picked up in a feral state. Like mustangs and brumbies in other continents,

Rameses II returning in triumph from the Battle of Kadesh. In this rock-relief inscribed on the walls of the temple of Karnak, the king is represented returning from the war with his prisoners

perhaps after several generations of regained freedom, being the descendants of mares and stallions in Mesopotamian and other Royal studs, that had been overwhelmed in some military or political catastrophe, they had eluded the efforts of the invaders or revolutionaries to catch them, and run loose on the desert. After all, we have seen such things happen, or almost happen, in Europe in our day. Potraz is a Prussian – it might have happened to Trakehnen; it nearly happened to Lipizza.

To refute theorists who claim the Arabian is derived from some more primitive breed there is the evidence of pictorial records of unvarying type from the 18th dynasty to the present day. The earliest hieroglyph of a horse of perfect Arabian type appears on the tomb of Phiri the Egyptian; and here we may say begins the documented evidence of the purity of the breed. The hieroglyph depicts a compact horse with a small concave head set on an arched neck; the tail high-set and the whole indicative of spirited movement; all those characteristics in short that we look for in our Arabians today.

Only a breed pure in itself, could have so transmitted its unique type over the centuries. Lady Wentworth comments:

It is most interesting to observe how the horse from its earliest mention, was the object of unbounded admiration. Beautiful, fierce in battle, strong and *nobly bred*. The horse in the wilderness that stumbleth not, the horse bounding and snorting at the scent of battle, swifter than the eagle and undismayed by death.

'The horse in the wilderness' – this is the major chord in all literature and art composed and inspired by the Arabian horse. He is part of that strange fascination which the desert holds for men, and men who sought the grandeur of the desert found there too the horse of the desert.

Nejd is all the high-lying district in the centre of the Arabian peninsula, between the Persian Gulf and the Red Sea. It is the centre of Eastern history between the two great highways from the vast expanse of continental Asia towards the seas and civilization of Europe and the West.

It is important in this context to realise that this plateau, now largely a starved and forbidding semi-desert, was once 'a land of rains and running waters'.

Over the years the gradual denudation of the soil, of herbage and moisture, lack of rainfall and the increase in locust-swarms, phenomena which have been observed in other parts of the world at the same period, have inexorably changed the whole mode of living of the Bedouin nomad tribes, who had for centuries inhabited this area.

Early in the 19th century travellers from Europe, taking advantage of greater facilities in transport, and a more settled political climate, began to explore a country which by reason of its terrain had been almost inaccessible to the traveller who feared danger and discomfort, and because of the frugal life of its inhabitants which offered no riches except a breed of horses legendary for their beauty. Because of the legendary nature of much of our information today it is important that we should record the impressions of such travellers, who by their background of knowledge, and the integrity of their purpose can best afford us a picture of the country and its people. Burckhardt, writing about 1820:

It is a general but erroneous opinion that Arabia is very rich in horses; the breed is limited to the extent of fertile pasture grounds in that country, and it is in such parts only that horses thrive, while those Bedouins who occupy districts of poor soil rarely possess any horses. It is found, accordingly, that the tribes most rich in horses are those who dwell in the comparatively fertile plains of Mesopotamia, and on the banks of the river Euphrates. Horses can there feed for several of the spring months upon the green grass and herbs produced by the rains in the valleys and fertile grounds . . .

In Hedjaz, especially in the mountainous regions of that country, and thence on towards Yemen, but few horses are to be seen, and these few are imported from the North. The Aeneze tribes on the frontiers of Syria have from eight to ten thousand horses; and some smaller tribes roving about that neighbourhood, possess, probably, half as many.

To the single tribe of Montefek Arabs, in the desert watered by the river Euphrates, we may assign at least eight thousand horses, and the tribes of Dhofyre and Beni Shammar are proportionately rich in these noble quadrupeds . . .

The settled inhabitants of Hedjaz and Yemen are not much in the habit of keeping horses – the great heat of the climate in Oman is reckoned unfavourable to the breeding of horses, which are there still more scarce than in Yemen.

The best pasturing places of Arabia not only produce the greatest number of horses, but likewise the finest and most select race. The best Koheyls of the khamsa are found in Nejd, on the Euphrates.

Both the climate and pasture of Yemen are reckoned injurious to the health of horses; many of them die from disease in that country, where they never thrive; indeed, the race begins to fall off in the very first generation.

Respecting the pedigrees of Arabian horses I must here add, that in the interior of the desert the Bedouins never refer to any among themselves; for they as well know the whole genealogy of their horses, as they do that of the owners. But when they take their horses to market at any town, such as Basra, Baghdad, Aleppo, Damascus, Medinah or Mecca, they carry along with them a written pedigree, which they present to the purchaser.

The Bedouins in general do not allow their mares to breed until they have completed their fifth year; but the poorer classes, who are eager for the profits arising from the sale of foals, sometimes wait no longer than the completion of the fourth year.

The Wahabi Chief, Saoud, who possesses, indisputably, the finest stud of horses in the whole East, never allows his mares to be mounted until they have completed their fourth year. The common Bedouins, however, frequently ride them even before they have attained their third year.

The Bedouins never allow a foal, at the moment of its birth, to fall upon the ground; they receive it in their arms, and so cherish it for several hours,

Arab horse of Nejd

occupied in washing and stretching its tender limbs, and caressing it as they would a baby. After this they place it on the ground, and watch its feeble steps with particular attention, prognosticating from that time the excellencies or defects of their future companion.

Abd-el-Kader was an Arab chieftain, Emir of the Southern Districts of Algiers, of high rank and celebrated for his learning; a great horseman and born leader of cavalry, and the mind and genius of a great general. He kept the French at bay from 1831 until 1847, when he surrendered. He was remembered as a hero in the eyes of the English for many years.

In a letter to General Daumas, the French Consul at Mascara accredited to the Emir from 1837 to 1839, he wrote:

To our friend General Daumas. Peace be with you!
Know then that amongst us it is admitted that Allah created the horse out of the wind, as he created Adam out of earth.

What the horse most yearns after is the combat and the race.

Now whence come the Arab people of the present day? It is related by many historians that – the first man who, after Adam mounted the horse was Ishmael, the father of the Arab race. He was the son of Lord Abraham, beloved of Allah.

There is a tradition that some Arabs of the Anzed tribe went up to Jerusalem the noble, to congratulate Solomon on his marriage with the Queen of Saba – Solomon thereupon gave orders to bring from his stable a magnificent stallion descended from Ishmael stock, and then dismissed them. These Arabs on their return home devoted him to foal-getting. This is the stock whose high renown has spread in the course of time through the whole world.

You ask by what outward signs the Arabs recognise a horse to be noble, a drinker of air. Here is my answer.

The horse of pure descent is distinguished among us by the thinness of its lips and of the interior cartilage of the nose; by the dilation of the nostrils; by the leanness of the flesh encircling the veins of the head; by the graceful

The Coming Storm, by Abraham Cooper

manner the neck is attached, by the softness of its coat, its mane, and the hairs of its tail; by its breadth of chest; the largeness of its joints, and the leanness of its extremities.

According, however, to the tradition of our ancestors, the Arabian horse is still better known by its moral characteristics than its physical peculiarities. The thoroughbred horses have no vice.

If a horse or a mare has given indisputable proof of extraordinary speed, or remarkable endurance of hunger and thirst; of rare intelligence, or of grateful affection for the hand that feeds them, the Arabs will make every sacrifice to obtain its progeny.

It is by means of his horse that the Arab holds whatever he possesses; rushes on his enemy, tracks him down or flees from him, and defends his family and his freedom.

Let him be enriched with possession of all that sweetens life, his horse alone is his protector.

Do you understand the boundless affection the Arab feels for his horse? It is only equalled by the services rendered by the latter.

Peace be with you at the end as at the beginning of this letter on the part of your friend, Abd-el-Kader Ben Mahhiden

Some further observations by the Emir Abd-el-Kader have been recorded by E. Daumas in *The Horses of the Sahara*, published in 1863:

The horse the most esteemed is a black one with a star on his forehead and white spots on his feet. Then comes the blood-bay, and after that the dark chestnut.

The Prophet has said: 'If thou woulds't go to war, purchase a horse with a star on his forehead and stockings on all his legs with the exception of the right forefoot.'

A horse with white feet, his off foreleg being alone the colour of his coat, resembles a man who carries himself gracefully in walking, with the sleeve of his coat floating in the air.

The fleetest of horses is the chestnut; the most enduring, the bay; the most spirited, the black; the most blessed, one with a white forehead.

OBSERVATIONS ON CHOOSING AND PURCHASING HORSES

In the Sahara horses that are celebrated for their blood and speed sell easily and at a good price. There are blemishes that totally exclude a horse from serving in war. Such as *el maateuk*, a narrow and hollow chest accompanying lean and perpendicular shoulders. It is difficult to form an idea of the importance attached by the Arabs to the development of the muscles of the chest.

Another blemish is fatness and want of prominence in the withers. You can never fix the saddle properly on such a horse, nor handle him boldly in galloping down hill. An animal is also rejected if he cannot see at night, or when there is snow. It is discovered by the manner he raises his feet when it begins to grow dark. The defect may be ascertained by placing a black surface before him in the day-time – if he steps upon it without hesitation, there is no doubt on the subject. As the Arab passes much of his life-time in making nocturnal marches to surprise his enemy, or to escape from him, what could he do with such an animal?

Let us pass on now to the faults or blemishes which, though generally avoided, do not prevent a horse from changing masters. These are narrow nostrils – they will leave you in trouble; long, soft and pendant ears; and a short stiff neck. A horse is little worth that does not lie down, nor one that switches his tail about while in quick motion; also horses that scratch their neck with their feet, that rest on the toe of their foot, that over-reach themselves in trotting or galloping, or that cut themselves by knocking their feet together.

Beware of a horse that rears, refuses the spur, bites, is difficult to mount, and breaks away from his rider when the latter dismounts; these are all grave faults in war time. Leave to the pack-saddle a horse that is deaf.

The highest virtue in a horse is endurance, to which, in order to constitute a perfect animal, must be joined strength. Strength and wind are the two highest qualities of a horse. The absence of either is likely to affect his endurance and lower his spirit.

By sight, by smell, by hearing, a horse will warn his master of coming danger, even if he do not save him from it. He saith:

> *'Preserve me from what is in front,*
> *I will preserve thee from what is behind.'*

W. G. Palgrave, describing the horses of King Ibn Saoud of Nejd in 1862 writes:

Never have I seen or imagined so lovely a collection. Their stature was indeed somewhat low; I do not think any were above fifteen hands; fourteen appeared to me about their average; but they were so exquisitely well-shaped that want of greater size seemed hardly, if at all, a defect. A little, a very little saddle-backed, just the curve which indicates springiness without weakness; a head broad above and tapering down to a nose fine enough to verify the phrase of 'drinking from a pint-pot'.

A most intelligent and yet a singularly gentle look, full eye, sharp thornlike little ear, legs fore and hind that seemed as if made of hammered iron, so clean and yet so well twisted with sinew; a neat round hoof, just the requisite for hard ground; a tail set on or rather thrown out at a perfect arch; coats smooth,

Arab horse of Shammar

shining and light; the mane long, but not overgrown nor heavy. The prevailing colour was chestnut or grey. But if asked what are the specially distinctive points of the Nejdee horse? I should reply, the slope of the shoulder, the extreme cleanness of the shank, and the full rounded haunch, though every other part too has a perfection and a harmony unwitnessed (at least by my eyes) anywhere else.

Their appearance justified all reputation all value, all poetry.

Roger Upton describing the desert of Arabia and its people about the year 1878, writes:

The tribes of Bedaween are very numerous, some poorer, some very rich and powerful; collectively they are a great, free, rich, pastoral, and at the same time a warlike people, and have no exact parallel in history.

The Bedaween have laws of their own, a traditional code of morality strictly kept, a policy as between tribe and tribe, and a system of government in each tribe, and alliances which are faithfully observed.

The Bedaween are more inclined to hold their own than to become a dominating race, nor does it seem probable that they could ever be collected and bound together to form a kingdom under one sovereign head.

Yet a free, generous people, which have followed the same course of pastoral life for ages, of wealth sufficient for their wants, and strong enough to resist all aggression, is not to be condemned by those who have followed agriculture and commerce, nor can whole tribes and families of 'a great nation' be counted as outcasts or homeless vagabonds.

Such tribes as have either wholly or partially time to cultivate the soil are not to be compared with their strictly nomadic brethren in prosperity or standing. One who accompanied us on our visit to the Bedaween, and had used his influence to induce some to settle, to exchange their mares for ploughs, and had supplied them with money for seed, exclaimed with sorrow, 'I question if what I have done has been for their welfare'.

Lady Anne Blunt writing in 1879, records with some sadness:

Among the Sebaa themselves, who have maintained the ancient breeds in all their integrity, various accidents have concurred in diminishing the number of their mares.

Several seasons of drought and famine, within the last fifteen years, have reduced the prosperity of the tribes, and forced them to part with some of their best breeding stock.

This was the country and these were the people that nurtured and bred the Arabian horse. His perfection was evolved through the necessities of his owners; his personality was the result of their appreciation of his virtues.

Of all creatures domesticated by man, only the dog and the Arabian horse have fully shared his life.

But the deterioration, noted by Lady Anne, of the conditions of life among the Bedouin tribes, and even more markedly in the horses they bred increased during the next two decades. Erstwhile nomadic tribes were forced to attempt cultivation; the ready purchase of firearms replaced the use of spear and sword, and finally the tribal system which had ordered the lives of these dwellers in the desert for so many centuries had to adapt itself to the pressures of Western civilization; thus their way of life no longer had need for that unique creation of which it was the epitome; the Kehailan horse of Arabia.

Here is a picture in words of an Anazeh mare described by the Hon. F. Walpole early in the 19th century in his book *The Ansayrii*:

She was worthy of the pen of a Warburton or a Lamartine; clean gray, with black mane and tail, silvered at the end; her skin thin as a kid glove, and the long hair as fine as that which droops over the shoulder of beauty.

The eye was wild, bright and flashing; the nostrils full, almost bell-shaped; tall and strong, yet light and active, she well deserved her name – The Beautiful.

The Hon. Sir James Penn Boucaut early in the 20th century writes:

An impure breed could never have maintained its essential sameness and characteristics so uniformly for so many thousands of years as the Arab has done, nor would men of all nations have so uniformly and so universally praised an animal which was not of surpassing excellence. If he pass away by human folly, you will never see his like again.

The perfection of this horse of the desert might have been today but a legend; a poetic inspiration, or the faint echo of travellers' tales. But a link was forged which, though slight and threatened by uncertainties, would hold and keep the past and their heritage secure.

Chapter 2

They Dwell Among Princes

THE EARLIEST importations into England of Arabian horses may have been through the Crusaders, or as princely gifts from Spain and France, where it is reasonable to suppose they were imported still earlier from North Africa.

Even at this period it is evident that the Arabian had been recognised in Europe as the fastest breed of horse then in existence. Records of horses of a superior stock, light and speedy, as contrasted with the native heavy breeds, are mentioned as having been used for coursing, in England, France and Spain.

From the 13th century onwards the whole Arabian Peninsula and the adjoining countries of Syria, Irak, the Lebanon and North Africa lay under Turkish domination, with Egypt as the headquarters of provincial government. The Sultans of Turkey encouraged the establishment of breeding centres for Arabian horses in every province under their rule. The princely rulers of Egypt, Morocco, Syria, and Tunisia, men of wealth and culture, imported horses from Arabia to found their studs. The horses so bred were kept for cavalry, as well as for racing and other sports.

Records of such early importations while extolling the value of particular horses, or speaking of their performance and value, seldom give us exact information of their conformation or their subsequent history.

We have to wait till 1333 to find an authentic and carefully documented record of importations from Arabia, made by the Mameluke Sultan, El Naseri.

Sultan El Malek El Naser Mohammed Kalaon of Egypt (A.D. 1290–1342) not only loved the Arab horse above all others; he appreciated its value in blood as well as in beauty, and for this reason would not hesitate to pay any sum asked in order to obtain horses of the highest quality, rather than take them by force in warfare, or by unjust means.

The prices he paid in gold and lands have never been equalled, and this generosity and fair dealing (he is said to have paid £1,000 and £7,000 for individual horses) were held in such high repute that no tribe in the desert would hesitate to obtain for him the best horses available. His importations were carefully recorded with a detailed history of every horse; written in Arabic, this record still exists.

At his death, we are told that the Sultan El Naseri owned three thousand horses, but his passion and his life's work came to naught, whether by neglect or the outbreak of a horse epidemic we cannot be sure, and all that remains is the wonderfully exact and illuminating record of his Stud.

The second notable importation of horses from Arabia was in the 19th century; though numerically not as great as that of the Sultan El Naseri, it is of greater importance today.

*Horse of His Highness
Abbas Pasha I*

In 1815 Mohammed Ali, Turkish ruler of Egypt, sent his army under the leadership of his son Ibrahim Pasha, to quell the rising power of the Wahabis in Nejd.

At the successful conclusion of the campaign Ibrahim Pasha returned to Egypt taking with him about two hundred of the finest mares and stallions captured from Riad and other cities in Nejd.

When the victorious army returned, a triumphant procession of the victors and their spoils entered Cairo, headed by twelve magnificent Nejdi stallions in golden trappings and led by Wahabi captives.

Watching that procession in wonder and admiration was a small boy named Abbas, son of an Egyptian Pasha, and nephew of Ibrahim Pasha.

The horses captured from Nejd, representing the finest blood in the desert were added to Mohammed Ali's Stud; some of them were given away as presents to other noblemen and governors of provinces and there can be little doubt that Tousson Pasha, father of Abbas, received such recognition.

A second and larger punitive expedition into Arabia by Ibrahim Pasha in 1819 captured Toureyf and with it the entire Stud of the Wahabi king, Saoud. The horses brought back furnished Ibrahim Pasha with enough stock to establish his own stud.

Here then, were two great Studs possessed of the finest blood of the desert strains which might have perpetuated and established the Arabian horse to the benefit of the East, and beyond.

Yet, as if the curse of the dispossessed owners still pursued those who had robbed them of their precious heritage, neither the Stud of Mohammed Ali, nor of Ibrahim Pasha, prospered.

Egypt never had been a successful horse-breeding country. Lack of pasture; flies, vermin of every kind, plagues peculiar to horses and cattle, heat, sand, lack of pure water, and above all the native ignorance and indifference to suffering could not encourage or maintain any such establishment, which to be successful required a high degree of knowledge and devoted care.

Travellers in Egypt at that time who were granted the privilege of visiting the Studs of Mohammed Ali and Ibrahim Pasha were unanimous in their admiration of the beautiful specimens of Arabian horses assembled there, and equally critical of the wretched conditions under which the horses were kept. Inevitably the numbers and quality of the stock deteriorated; some were given as presents to foreign rulers, some were sold, an unrecorded number died, but Fate played a part in the survival of the rest.

Abbas Pasha, the boy who had watched with wonder and admiration the captive stallions from Arabia, had in the years since then sought out and obtained from several sources, horses which fulfilled in his eyes his youthful dream of perfection. Being the grandson of Mohammed Ali he was in an advantageous position to see, and be enabled to acquire, the best.

During the years of decline of the Studs of his grandfather Mohammed Ali, and his uncle Ibrahim Pasha, Abbas tried to save by purchase all he could of their horses.

In 1836, when he was 23, Abbas Pasha became the first Viceroy of Egypt.

He must have been a young man of considerable imagination, foresight, and generosity. Still determined to acquire by all means the best blood of the desert, he planned the escape of the Wahabi prince, Feysul Ibn Saoud, who had been kept prisoner in the citadel at Cairo for four years by Abbas Pasha's grandfather, Mohammed Ali.

The price of his escape? That Feysul would deliver, as ransom, the pick of desert mares, including Feysul's famous Jellabieh mare for which Abbas generously gave him £7,000.

Thus, the boy Abbas had seen his dream fulfilled. Forty years later the horses he had collected were spoken of all over the Egyptian provinces with wonder, and tales told of their beauty and of their incalculable value.

As Viceroy of Egypt he was able to send his emissaries to all the horse breeding centres in Arabia and the provinces under Turkish rule, and the prices given for such horses as he desired became as legendary as their superb excellence.

He built a magnificent palace in the desert at Dar-el-Bayda, in the country between Cairo and Suez, with every refinement for the comfort and well-being of his horses. It is said that in its best years his Stud comprised a thousand horses. No one place could have supplied water for so many animals, so they were dispersed among three or four establishments built especially for them. At Dar-el-Bayda which stood on an eminence, Abbas Pasha himself lived so that he would continuously enjoy the sight of his horses.

The importance of the Abbas Pasha Stud can hardly be overestimated in the history of the Arabian horse. First, the purity of the stock he obtained was without doubt authentic.

Pedigrees are not recorded in writing among desert tribes, but by sending a trustworthy scribe, it was possible to record the pedigrees from the statements of their owners, and this was done before witnesses of the tribe who would confirm or negate the statements so given. Thus it can be considered as without doubt that only horses of unquestioned purity were in the Abbas Pasha Stud.

Secondly, the Viceroy must have been a connoisseur of rare distinction. While descriptions of other historically famous Studs note the speed and racing achievements of their inmates, visitors to the Abbas Pasha Stud describe only the extraordinary beauty and majesty of his horses.

So anxious was he to preserve their type that he engaged Bedouins from Arabia of high birth and position, capable not only of watching over and directing the management of his Stud on strictly Bedouin lines, but also of checking the accounts given of genealogies, and so of precluding any chance of error.

One might think that here at last had been laid the sure foundations that would establish the Arabian breed, guard its purity of blood, and preserve its type and quality in unassailable conditions, so that posterity might reap the advantage.

Yet, like some shimmering mirage of the desert, this achievement, the life-work of a man of wealth and vision, was to dissolve and vanish, leaving only glittering fragments as proof of its existence.

In 1854 Abbas Pasha was assassinated. It is not difficult to imagine the immediate political repercussions of such an event, nor the period of unrest and intrigue that inevitably followed.

Abbas Pasha's son, El Hami Pasha inherited his father's estate and his Stud, but he had neither the ability of his father nor his interest in breeding, and was moreover so heavily in debt that he could not support the establishment.

El Hami died three years after coming into his inheritance, and the priceless collection of horses of Abbas Pasha was broken up and sold by auction. About 200 horses went to European countries, Arab-racing being then at the height of its popularity, and many European Kings and Principalities with their own establishments were eager to avail themselves of a new source of desert blood to reinforce and improve their own lines of breeding. Few of these European-bred, or blended lines has left any impression on the breeding of Arabs to equal that of one stallion, the direct descendant of one of the Abbas Pasha horses taken to Turkey, who came by way of France and Poland to England early in the 20th century, and whose blood is woven like a thread of gold through the pedigrees of the finest Arabians of our day.

A frequent visitor of note to the Abbas Pasha Stud in the days of its glory, was one Ali Pasha Sherif. He must have been a man of like mind, and it would seem

Horse of Ali Pasha Sherif

from subsequent events a man well-versed in the pedigrees and value of individual animals. At the dispersal sale of the Abbas Pasha Stud after El Hami Pasha's death, Ali Pasha Sherif, now Governor of Syria, bought a large part of the Stud and devoted to its re-establishment his knowledge, and his personal fortune.

In 1873 it is on record that Ali Pasha Sherif's Stud consisted of nearly four hundred horses of the highest quality which he had bred from the stock acquired from Abbas Pasha, thus carrying on the tradition and the veritable breed and blood-lines of the desert.

But now, again, disaster struck from an unexpected quarter. In 1880, an outbreak of horse sickness of virulent form spread over lower Egypt and the adjoining Provinces, and in the epidemic many strains of Ali Pasha's Stud were completely wiped out. He sent some of his horses to Upper Egypt and these alone were saved.

Some ten years later this magnificent Stud was on the point of dissolution, and its records are now only a landmark in the path of Arabian history.

The Pasha in his old age, was caught up in the intrigues of his sons, who, anxious to save their inheritance which they believed their father was spending needlessly, arranged for the Stud to be sold.

Ali Pasha Sherif, now practically a prisoner in their hands, died heart broken, a few weeks after his horses were auctioned.

But the link still held.

In that period which saw the rise and fall of Ali Pasha Sherif's greatness, two English travellers were exploring Arabia and the land of the Euphrates, drawn by that mysterious attraction which the desert and its way of life has held for the European for centuries.

These travellers were better fitted for their expedition than perhaps any who had preceded them. They were wealthy, aristocratic, with influence in political circles which was to be of great help in the future carrying out of their design, and above all they came with minds aware of what they might expect to find; appreciative of the peculiar beauty and characteristics of the land, and with a sensitive perception which enabled them to compare and to record their impressions in writing and in art.

The travellers were Mr. Wilfrid Scawen Blunt and his wife Lady Anne Blunt. It was not their first visit to an Arabic speaking country; indeed they were already seasoned travellers. In her diaries, *Bedouin Tribes of the Euphrates*, Lady Anne records:

There had, indeed, been a sort of progression in our travels and we had been carried by them always further and further eastwards, passing from Spain to Barbary, and from Barbary to Egypt, and thence to Syria, so that it was natural that the Euphrates valley and Mesopotamia should be chosen as the scene of our next campaign.

Wilfred Scawen Blunt in
Arab dress, by Tristram
Ellis, 1884

The Blunts, like many members of the British aristocracy of that period, had bred and owned, ridden, and raced horses for generations. Moreover the use of Arabian blood to improve the English racehorse was a custom already established in their family. Sir James D'Arcy, a common ancestor of the Blunt and Wentworth families, had imported Arabian stallions and mares early in the 17th century, and Sir Ralph Milbanke, ancestor of Lady Anne Blunt, established in the 18th century a foundation Stud of Eastern blood.

The old Morocco Mare, the Moonah Barb Mare, the Darcy White Turk, the Darcy Yellow Turk, and the Darcy Royal mares, are names of the foundation stock from these two Studs all of which are found today in the pedigrees of our most famous thoroughbreds.

To the Blunts, this horse of the desert was the epitome of perfection. Though well acquainted with it in history, literature and art, in their travels they set themselves to discover all they could of its unique reality. Like many other

Europeans they believed that the Bedouin tribes would not part with their mares to foreigners, but nevertheless they determined to discover if, by any means, the source of the pure, the authentic Arabian blood could be found and procured.

They were singularly suited to this task by nature of their mutual tastes; love of beauty, harmony of form and colour, and a regard for the romance and the achievements of a more heroic age.

They could not have known that their quest for the Arabian horse was to have a profound effect not only on their own lives, but in the very survival of the breed.

In the last and most memorable journey among the horse-breeding tribes of the desert, which Lady Anne Blunt has described in detail in her diaries, it is evident how, by completely identifying themselves with the people of the land; by adopting their speech, respecting their customs and beliefs, and appreciating their virtues rather than criticising their weaknesses, they in their turn were accorded the respect and the dignities given to the princely sheiks of the tribal families.

In the matter of acquiring horses the Blunts appeared to have had little difficulty. They chose the best of such as were possible to obtain and were generous in the prices they paid, and in all their transactions there appeared to be a simplicity and integrity in complete accord with the desert traditions of honourable dealing and brotherhood among equals. It is evident in their writings that the Blunts could foresee the events which would lead to the virtual extinction of the horse-breeding tribes and their way of life, and they were possessed with the imaginative idea of founding, on the soil and in the climate which they supposed would be most favourable, a Stud to maintain their desert-bred horses. About 1881 they purchased a house standing in a neglected garden, and about thirty acres of land on the outskirts of Cairo and ten miles distant from that city, called Ain Shems. Here, on desert soil they planned to establish their Stud, 'Sheykh Obeyd'.

Additional buildings were erected, the land was ploughed and watered and a system of irrigation installed. A Bedouin, one 'Zeyd' of the Muteyr tribe of Nejd was appointed keeper of the stables.

Writing in 1888, Wilfrid Blunt describes the peace and beauty of this garden in the desert:

I did not remain more than a few days at Cairo on arrival, but went on to my country place at Sheykh Obeyd, ten miles distant outside the town, where I got the little garden house ready for my wife and daughter to inhabit; a beautiful retired place on the desert edge far from European intrusion, standing on the old pilgrim camel-track where it branches off to Syria, and little frequented except by the Arab horse merchants, who bring their horses for sale each spring to Cairo.

There we lived in seclusion and very happily for the three winter months, building and enlarging the house and recovering the garden from the neglected state into which it had fallen.

In November 1900 he described the countryside in Egypt in winter:

There are few things more beautiful than the Delta at this time of year. The appearance of plenty and happiness does one good after the squalor of Europe. The country districts are still quite untouched by our Western ugliness. On the whole journey from Alexandria I did not see a European or a European dress, yet the fields were full of people, with their buffaloes and donkeys and camels crowding the country roads; men, women, and children gathering cotton in manifest enjoyment of their lives. The splendid wealth, too, of the crops, especially the maize, delights one. Then there are the birds; I counted nine kingfishers, some blue, some pied, and as many hoopoes. . . . I was met by my mare and Mutlak at the station and rode through the moonlit garden which was alive with cicalas, and so enjoyed its whole beauty.

Sheykh Obeyd was not the only Arabian Stud in that part of the country; visits were interchanged with other establishments and the Blunts frequently entertained distinguished visitors from Europe as well as from Egypt. Mr. Blunt has written some interesting comments on Arabians in other Studs:

28th April 1893
    In the evening we drove to the Sweet Waters and were shown the Sultan's mares. There were, I believe, about 150 of them, all mares from the Arabs, but the greater part of them of very small account. Among the herd, however, one was able to pick out about a dozen really good ones, and two or three of the first class. But there was no mare there at all equal to Ali Pasha Sherif's best, or the best of our own. The best I found had come from Ibn Rashid, who, two years ago, sent thirty. But the Egyptian who manages the establishment tells me that they will insist upon tall horses, and I fancy the Bedouins who send the Sultan

Lady Anne Blunt at Sheykh Obeyd

Azz (mare)

Antar (stallion)

mares get the big ones on purpose for him, and keep the little ones, which are the best. There was a great hulking mare which Sotamm Ibn Shaalan had brought with him, one I feel sure was never foaled among the Roals. Of horses they showed us seven, the best being without comparison a Seglawi of Ali Pasha Sherif's, an exact match to our Shahwan. This was a really beautiful and perfect horse, but of diminuitive size compared with the others, and so less esteemed here, though the Egyptian knew his worth. Next to him was an immensely showy chestnut from Ferhan Jerba, a beautifully topped horse of great quality, but a little overgrown, and, so the manager told me, less good at the stud than the other. Beyond these two there was not one I would have cared to own, two or three of them being quite unfit to breed from. The management of the stud is, I fancy, very defective, so there were certainly four mares out of five barren. There is, however, enough material to make a good stud out of. I should pick out twenty of the best and sell the others. There were a good many black mares among them, sent as rarities, but I doubt if black is ever a good Arab colour. One of these came from Ibn Rashid and was the best; Sarah Bernhardt was also in the paddock looking on.

29th April 1893

In the afternoon we went with the Walter Blunts to see the Sultan's stables at Yildiz; first, however, to call on the director of it, Izzat Pasha, the most European Oriental I have ever met. We found him in trouble, his son having

Ghadia (mare)

attempted to commit suicide the day before through a love affair. He talked of this quite as a European might. He was sitting in his house near Yildiz, in a rough kind of smoking suit, his hair en brosse, and no fez – rather a picturesque looking man, who might have been a French or Italian artist. One certainly would never have guessed him an Oriental. He talked a good deal of heresy about horse-breeding, declared that nine out of ten Arabs had unsound hocks (an absurdity), and they were all unsound one way or the other. He says there is hardly a horse or mare sent by the Bedouins to the Sultan which would pass a veterinary examination. This may perhaps be true, as I daresay they pass on their unsound ones when they are making presents, to say nothing of the horses they send getting changed on their road to Constantinople.

At the stables, which are inside Yildiz Park wall, we found a splendid collection of stallions arranged in stalls according to their colours, gray, black, or bay – very few chestnuts. Among these the most remarkable were, I think, half-a-dozen brought by Nasr el Ashgar, Sheykh of the Montefik, and several very fine ones from Mohammed Ibn Rashid and others presented singly by Walys of Bagdad. There were some enormously powerful horses among the bays, and one very fine black horse from Ibn Rashid. But there was unfortunately no intelligent person to explain, nor anybody who knew Arabic, except a black slave. In the first stable there were about sixty horses, nearly all of high quality, but we could not have more than two or three led out, so it was impossible really to judge them. Beyond these were a couple of hundred more,

Ghazieh (mare)

inferior ones, in another stable, and yet a third and fourth stable with European animals. A very old white Arab horse was shown us as the Sultan's favourite for riding, but they say he seldom gets on horseback. Altogether the grandest Arab collection I have seen, and far superior in quality to the mares we saw yesterday.

17th April 1894

To Koubbah Palace (Abbas' country residence, three miles from Sheykh Obeyd). I was taken to the garden and found Abbas sitting under some trees near the stables inspecting mares which were being paraded before him. With

Jamil (stallion)

him was the old Soudanese, Mohammed Taher, whom the Khedive introduced to me as a loyal Shaggia. We talked first about the horses, six of them for which Abbas said he was offering £800. But only two of them were good ones. These were a brown mare, like our Queen of Sheba, and a little gray with a fine shoulder, perfectly level back, and tail grandly carried.

To return now to the declining fortunes of Ali Pasha Sherif and the dissolution of his Arabian Stud. The Blunts were well acquainted with the Stud, they had seen it in its best days and Lady Anne, in her diaries has noted the horses there at some length having bought some as early as 1889.

Of these Mr. Blunt records:

Today two three-year-old colts and a filly arrived at the garden (Ain Shems),
which I have bought of Ali Pasha Sherif, all three of the Viceroy Abbas Pasha's
stock, one colt and a Jellabiet filly; the other a Saqlawi Ibn Soudan. This last
(Mesaoud) ought to be valuable some day for our Stud in England. Ali Pasha's
horses are the only ones of pure Arabian breed in Egypt, and there are certain
points about them superior to all others.

On one of their last visits they describe the sad deterioration that had come
about:

We saw Ali Pasha's Stud in the last hours of its disruption. Decimated by plague
and weakened by years of inbreeding and gross neglect, the horses were of an
ethereal quality and truly like gazelles, and with no more bone. It was 'Type'
etherealised almost to extinction.

Yet the sight of these old snow-white stallions remains as an undying memory
of proud necks and tails, and a spirit which no starvation could kill. Absorbed
in their beauty there was no room to criticise the sad frailness of frame, the
startled expression of the deer-like eyes brought suddenly into sunlight from
the blackness of what seemed an underground stable.

The arched gateways of the palace courtyards formed an impressive setting
as each horse was led out. Perhaps the finest were Mahruss and Aziz, and two
snow-white stallions, Ibn Nadir and another smaller but truly perfect horse of
amazing beauty, but fragile to the last degree.

Saadun (stallion)

The final dissolution of Ali Pasha Sherif's Stud took place in 1897. The horses that were still fit to be of any use were sold by auction and of these *the best were purchased by the Blunts*. The earliest of the desert-bred horses had already been established in England at the Crabbet and Newbuildings estates in Sussex, the ancestral home of the Blunts. Their later purchases in the desert and some from Ali Pasha Sherif were kept at Sheykh Obeyd, where the numbers were limited to about fifty. The greater number went to Crabbet, among them: Mahruss, Aziz, Merzuk, Kasida, Makbula, Wazir, Jellabieh, Balis, Hilmeyeh, Feysul, and Bint Nura. Lady Anne has recorded a list of the horses at Ain Shems in the year 1907, with notes on their strains and breeding:

SHEYKH OBEYD STUD

Brood mares and fillies, the produce of mares originally brought from Arabia.

Seglawi Jedran

1. Ghazala, White mare, foaled about June, 1896, a Seglawieh Jedranieh of Ibn Sudan's strain of the Roala tribe (No. 8 in Sheykh Obeyd Stud Book), bred by Ali Pasha Sherif in Cairo. Dam, Bint Helwa, a White Seglawieh Jedranieh of Ibn Sudan's strain (No. 1 in Sheykh Obeyd Stud Book, No. 66 in Crabbet Arabian Stud Book). Sire, Ibn Sherara, a white Kehilan Ajuz of the Jellabi strain, or Kehilan Jellabi. Both dam and sire bred by Ali Pasha Sherif, and descended from mares and horses brought from Arabia to Egypt by Abbas Pasha I, Viceroy of Egypt.

2. Ghadia, Grey mare foaled March 3rd, 1904, a Seglawieh Jedranieh of Ibn Sudan's strain of the Roala tribe (No. 22 in Sheykh Obeyd Stud Book). Dam, Ghazala (see above No. 1). Sire, Feysul, a chestnut Kehilan Ajuz of the Jellabi strain, or Kehilan Jellabi (No. 6 in Sheykh Obeyd Stud Book, No. 27 in Crabbet Arabian Stud Book), bred by Ali Pasha Sherif.

3. Grey filly, foaled about November, 1906, a Seglawieh Jedranieh of Ibn Sudan's strain of the Roala tribe. Dam, Ghazala (see above No. 1). Sire, Jamil, a Chestnut Seglawi Jedran of Ibn Sbeyni's strain (No. 8 in Sheykh Obeyd Stud Book), bred by Ali Pasha Sherif (see No. 4 Horses).

4. Ghazieh, Bay mare, foaled early in March, 1897, a Seglawieh Jedranieh of Ibn Sudan's strain of the Roala tribe (No. 15 in Sheykh Obeyd Stud Book), bred by Ali Pasha Sherif. Dam, Bint Horra, a white Seglawieh Jedranieh of Ibn Sudan's strain (No. 9 in Sheykh Obeyd Stud Book). Sire, Ibn Nura, a white Dahman Nejib (No. 5 in Sheykh Obeyd Stud Book). Both dam and

sire bred by Ali Pasha Sherif and descended from mares and horses brought from Arabia to Egypt by Abbas Pasha I, Viceroy of Egypt.

5. Ghazwa, Chestnut mare, foaled October 28th, 1901, a Seglawieh Jedranieh of Ibn Sudan's strain of the Roala tribe (No. 21 in Sheykh Obeyd Stud Book). Dam Ghazieh (see above No. 4). Sire Feysul, a Chestnut Kehilan Ajuz of the Jellabi strain or Kehilan Jellabi (No. 6 in Sheykh Obeyd Stud Book, No. 27 in Crabbet Arabian Stud Book), bred by Ali Pasha Sherif.

6. Bay Filly, foaled January 24th, 1907, a Seglawieh Jedranieh of Ibn Sudan's strain of the Roala tribe. Dam, Ghazieh (see above No. 4). Sire, Jamil, a chestnut Seglawi Jedran of Ibn Sbeyni's strain of the Mehed tribe of Fedaan (No. 4, Horses).

7. Fasiha, Grey (fleabitten) mare, foaled 1892, a Seglawieh Jedranieh of Ibn Sbeyni's strain of the Mehed tribe of Fedaan (No. 4 in Sheykh Obeyd Stud Book), bred by Ali Pasha Sherif, Dam, Bint Fereyha el Saghira, a grey (fleabitten) Seglawieh Jedranieh of Ibn Sbeyni's strain (No. 3 in Sheykh Obeyd Stud Book). Sire, Ibn Sherara, a white Kehilan Ajuz of the Jellabi strain or Kehilan Jellabi. Both dam and sire bred by Ali Pasha Sherif and descended from mares and horses brought from Arabia to Egypt by Abbas Pasha I, Viceroy of Egypt.

8. Aziza, Chestnut mare, foaled April 2nd 1900, at Zeytun, near Cairo (her dam being then in possession of M. Suares), a Seglawieh Jedranieh of Ibn Sbeyni's strain of the Mehed tribe of Fedaan (No. 19 in Sheykh Obeyd Stud Book). Dam, Bint Jamila, a white Seglawieh Jedranieh of Ibn Sbehni's strain (No. 18 in Sheykh Obeyd Stud Book). Sire, Aziz, a chestnut Dahman Shahwan. Both dam and sire bred by Ali Pasha Sherif and descended from mares and horses brought from Arabia to Egypt by Abbas Pasha I, Viceroy of Egypt.

Dahman Shahwan

9. Azz, White mare, foaled 1895. A Dahmeh Shahwanieh of the strain belonging to Ibn Khalifeh, Sheykh of Bahreyn on the Eastern coast of Arabia (No. 23 in Sheykh Obeyd Stud Book), bred by Ali Pasha Sherif in Cairo. Dam, Bint Azz, a white Dahmeh Shahwanieh of the strain belonging to Ibn Khalifeh. Sire, Ibn Nura, the white (fleabitten) Dahman Nejib (No. 5 in Sheykh Obeyd Stud Book). Both dam and sire bred by Ali Pasha Sherif and descended from mares and horses brought from Arabia to Egypt by Abbas Pasha I, Viceroy of Egypt.

Kehilan Ajuz (of which all other Kehilans are offshoots)

10. Kerima, Chestnut mare, foaled March, 1897, a Kehilet Ajuz of the Jellabi strain belonging to Ibn Kahlifeh, Sheykh of Bahreyn on the Eastern coast of Arabia or Kehileh Jellabieh (No. 16 in Sheykh Obeyd Stud Book). Dam, Makbula (should be 'Bint Makbula') a white Kehileh Jellabieh (No. 7 in Sheykh Obeyd Stud Book, No. 72 in Crabbet Arabian Stud Book). Sire, Aziz, a Chestnut Dahman Shahwan of the strain belonging to Ibn Khalifeh, Sheykh of Bahreyn on the Eastern coast of Arabia. Both dam and sire bred by Ali Pasha Sherif and descended from mares and horses brought from Arabia to Egypt by Abbas Pasha I, Viceroy of Egypt.

11. Chestnut Filly, foaled January 10th, 1907, a Kehilet Ajuz of the Jellabi strain belonging to Ibn Khalifeh, Sheykh of Bahreyn on the Eastern coast of Arabia, or Kehileh Jellabieh. Dam, Kerima (see above, No. 10). Sire, Jamil, a chestnut Seglawi Jedran of Ibn Sbeyni's strain of the Mehed tribe of Fedaan (No. 4, Horses).

HORSES

Seglawi Jedran

1. Ghadir, Grey colt, foaled February, 1905, a Seglawi Jedran of Ibn Sudan's strain of the Roala tribe. Dam, Ghazala (No. 1 mares, and No. 8 in Sheykh Obeyd Stud Book). Sire, Feysul, a Chestnut Kehilan Ajuz of the Jellabi strain or Kehilan Jellabi (No. 6 in Sheykh Obeyd Stud Book, and No. 27 in Crabbet Arabian Stud Book), bred by Ali Pasha Sherif in Cairo.

2. Ghanim, Chestnut colt, foaled in August, 1904, a Seglawi Jedran of Ibn Sudan's strain of the Roala tribe. Dam, Ghazieh No. 4 mares). Sire, Feysul, a chestnut Kehilan Ajuz of the Jellabi strain or Kehilan Jellabi (No. 6 in Sheykh Obeyd Stud Book, and No. 27 in Crabbet Arabian Stud Book) bred by Ali Pasha Sherif in Cairo.

3. Ghareb, Bay colt, foaled July 15th, 1905, a Seglawi Jedran of Ibn Sudan's strain of the Roala tribe. Dam, Ghazieh (No. 4 mares). Sire, Feysul, a chestnut Kehilan Ajuz of the Jellabi strain, or Kehilan Jellabi (No. 6 in Sheykh Obeyd Stud Book, and No. 27 in Crabbet Arabian Stud Book), bred by Ali Pasha Sherif in Cairo.

4. Jamil, Chestnut horse, foaled 1896, a Seglawi Jedran of Ibn Sbeyni's strain of the Mehed tribe of Fedaan (No. 8 in Sheykh Obeyd Stud Book) bred by Ali Pasha Sherif in Cairo. Dam, Bint Jamila (No. 18 in Sheykh Obeyd Stud Book. Sire, Aziz, a Chestnut Dahwan Shahwan. Both dam and sire bred

by Ali Pasha Sherif and descended from mares and horses brought from Arabia to Egypt by Abbas Pasha I, Viceroy of Egypt.

5. Ashoab, Grey colt, foaled November, 1905, a Seglawi Jedran of Ibn Sbeyni's strain of the Mehed tribe of Fedaan. Dam, Aziza (No. 8 mares, and No. 19 in Sheykh Obeyd Stud Book). Sire, Wubbr, a Grey Seglawi Jedran of Ibn Sbeyni's strain foaled, March 5th, 1897, his dam Bint Fereyha el Saghira (No. 3 in Sheykh Obeyd Stud Book), his sire Ibn Sherara, a white Kehilan Ajuz of the Jellabi strain or Kehilan Jellabi. Both dam and sire bred by Ali Pasha Sherif and descended from mares and horses brought from Arabia to Egypt by Abbas Pasha I, Viceroy of Egypt.

Kehilan Ajuz (of which all other Kehilans are offshoots)

6. Sarab, Chestnut colt, foaled early in October, 1905, a Kehilan Ajuz of the Jellabi strain or Kehilan Jellabi. Dam, Kerima (No. 8 mares, and No. 14 in Sheykh Obeyd Stud Book). Sire, Jamil, a Chestnut Seglawi Jedram of Ibn Sbeyni's strain (No. 8 in Sheykh Obeyd Stud Book), bred by Ali Pasha Sherif in Cairo (see No. 4 Horses).

In spite of their care for the welfare of their horses the Stud at Sheykh Obeyd was not an unqualified success. The heat, the insect pests, and above all the carelessness and neglect of the horses by their grooms while the Blunts were away in England made them decide to limit the stock kept there, and the bulk of the Stud was transferred to Crabbet Park.

Chapter 3
Land of Promise

WITH THE transfer of the greater part of the Stud from Egypt to England, the link was preserved.

From the desert, their native home, through generations of unbroken lineage and unassailable purity of blood, the precious legacy had come to rest at last. Or so it seemed: the Stud that would grow to be the most renowned of the 20th century had been established.

It became well known to visitors from abroad; at home people who were familiar with the Arabian horse in literature and art came for the first time to see the reality; the yearly sales of Crabbet stock conducted by Messrs. Tattersall became a function much sought after by London Society. Prices were not high by present-day standards, and the sales were made to individuals rather than as breeding stock, but some of those early purchases formed the nucleus of smaller studs for which breeders had cause to be grateful in later years.

The following memorandum by Wilfrid Blunt, written in July, 1897, is of value as it gives some information on horses retained by the Blunts as foundation stock:

The sources of the Crabbet breeding stock have been:

(1) The mares purchased by us in 1877–78 on the occasion of our first visit to Aleppo. These we procured with the assistance of Mr. Consul Skene. With the single exception of Sherifa, all were of Anazeh origin, Sherifa alone being a Nejd mare from the Stud of Feysul Ibn Saoud.

(2) The mares purchased by us on the occasion of our second visit to the Anazeh in 1881.

(3) Mares purchased at various times from the Stud of Ali Pasha Sherif in Egypt, principally in 1897.

(4) A few mares from other sources.

Of our original mares of 1877–78 we have preserved descendants only from five, viz, Queen of Sheba, Basilisk, Dajania, Jerboa and Sherifa. The rest either proved barren or have died out in the second generation, or their descendants have been discarded as inferior. Of the mares purchased we have descendants from: Meshura and Rodania, the rest having been weeded out.

All our Ali Pasha Sherif mares, being more recently purchased, are still alive either at Crabbet or at Sheykh Obeyd. They are: Khatila, Sobha, Bint Helwa, Bint Fereyha, Fasiha, Fulana, Badia, Makbula, Bint Horba, Ghazieh, Bint

Nura, Esh Shakra, Manolita, Johara.

Of the extraneous mares the only one of whom we have preserved descendants is Ferida.

·The imported horses which have given us descendants still at Crabbet are: from the Anazeh, Kars, Pharoah, Azrek: from Ali Pasha Sherif, Mesaoud, Merzuk, Shahwan.

Wilfred Scawen Blunt and Lady Anne Blunt in the library at Crabbet Park

Of the mares imported from Arabia and still represented at Crabbet all are strictly speaking of equal rank in point of blood, but the strains which have hitherto proved themselves the best are: 1. Rodania's 2. Dajania's through Nefisa; 3 and 4. Meshura's and Basilisk's; 5. Queen of Sheba's. Sherifa's descent has not yet produced a first class colt and Jerboa's is represented principally through Jeroboam's daughter Rosemary.

All the Ali Pasha Sherif mares are worthy in point of blood to give stallions to the Stud, but we have not sufficient experience yet to say which of the strains they represent is the best.

Of the stallions used at Crabbet by far our best has been Mesaoud. After him Azrek. Pharoah's blood, what we have of it, is excellent and should be carefully preserved, especially the strains through Bozra and Rosemary. Kars' blood seems less good, his best strain being through Rose Diamond. Merzuk's is represented only in Ridaa and it should be carefully preserved. A strain of Shahwan's blood too should be kept through Sobha.

The Blunts, who were well aware of the scarcity of first class horses in Arabia, always ascertained to their satisfaction that the horses they were using for breeding were truly authentic, and if they could not obtain the satisfaction they needed they were weeded out regardless of their qualities.

The Memorandum continues:

It must be remembered that fraud in the matter of pedigrees is of constant occurrence in the East and that certificates given for one horse are often transferred by unscrupulous dealers to another. The Crabbet Stud's supreme merit being that it is 'mazbut', of known pedigree in the whole of its original mares and horses.

The following extracts are from the copy of a letter written by Lady Anne Blunt in 1917, in reply to an American breeder who had asked for her opinion on various horses, and also whether any differences had shown in the Arab after breeding for two or three generations in England:

All this while to my regret I have been unable to write owing to the presence of one compulsory correspondence on the top of two, to complete that book of fragments concerning the Arabian horse.

This 'book of fragments' was never published as such, but it is the core of Lady Wentworth's book *The Authentic Arabian Horse*. Lady Anne Blunt's correspondence referred to here is largely in connection with a Trust she was hoping to set up in Egypt to assist National horse breeding by 'providing a centre of absolutely

The Blunts riding authentic pure blood to help encourage poor breeders and especially poor farmers'.

Lady Anne goes on to describe some horses:

I have a precious sister of his (Abu Zeyd) Rose of Hind, nearly 'own' sister as her sire was Rejeb by Mesaoud out of Rosemary. She too is first class and is the dam of Razaz by Astraled. I once saw Maidan at Miss Dillon's and that was a good head. Rosa Rugosa's head and profile comes (pedigree through Imamzada) from El Emir, a useful horse but of no Arab type, but Rose of Sharon seems to have been a good modifier and her colt Suleyman, by Abu Zeyd is most attractive.

By the way I must remark that my most successful stud sires, Razaz and Sotamm, both had fine action to which I attach great importance. The very few that lacked it, as did Shibim, I weeded out.

I have presented a stallion and two mares to the Government Department in Ajul – now they are moving heaven and earth to get true Arabians to help the cause. In Egypt there are hardly any beside what I have and none can be got from Arabia. Very few exist there owing to the casualties in the internal Bedouin warfare and the ever more restricted areas where the tribes have authentic pure breds. Since Davenport's visit things have gone from bad to worse in that respect. I know this because I daily see Nejd persons, Arabs who have for one cause or another settled in this country.

As to size, the descendants of Hadban (who was very small but with strength and an ideal head) through two mares, the only ones we have had of his having persistently reached 15 hands and over, in one case that of Rijm 15·3 out of Rose of Sharon, with substance to match, and his sire was quite small.

I have not systematically gone into the increase of height but what does increase is length generally and length of neck and shoulder particularly. There is no alteration of type.

The white socks all come from the celebrated Aziz of Abbas Pasha descent, bred by Ali Pasha Sherif – he was the sire of Mesaoud.

As to quality, the change of climate has not shown the slightest diminution indeed, if anything it appears to be more pronounced, and we do not carry out the Eastern custom of giving an upward jerk to the new born foal's tail or sewing its ears together with a piece of silken thread.

One very important aspect of the Crabbet Stud was the admission of Arabian horses in the General Stud Book, the prerogative of the Jockey Club hitherto reserved only for Thoroughbred race horses.

The late Mr. James Weatherby, owner and director of the General Stud Book, must have been convinced of the unquestionable purity of the stock imported by the Blunts; moreover he must have believed that an Arabian strain would be a valuable reserve out-cross in view of its proved value in the past; and in its possible use in the future to restore the deficiencies of inbred racing stock. A special section for pure-bred Arabs was added in Vol. XIV of the General Stud Book in 1881. The earliest entries in this section are all Blunt importations.

For the Blunts it seemed that the imaginative vision that had been born of their travels in the desert, the precious harvest of those journeyings, and all the advantages that wealth and their unique knowledge of the Arabian provided, should now have found its finest setting. And for a time it did. But with failing health and advancing years Mr. Blunt's judgment seemed to grow warped. The conduct of his private affairs, his financial commitments, and his disregard for the welfare of the Stud caused his wife, Lady Anne, ever increasing anxiety and distress. The politically troubled years which preceded the First World War were already casting lengthening shadows. To one who had known the peace of the desert, the storms of personal conflict must have been more difficult to bear than any physical hardship she had endured.

Much has been written, and even more has been imagined about the reasons for the decline of the Blunt Stud at Crabbet Park.

Two immovable facts against which all reasoning must eddy and break were these; the personality of Mr. Blunt, and the disintegration of the established order in the lives of people at the outbreak of the First World War.

Lady Wentworth, Wilfrid Blunt's daughter, in her book *The Authentic Arabian Horse*, sums up her father's personality in these words:

A man of brilliant genius, he was intolerant of law and discipline, impetuous and inconsistent, for while eloquently preaching the equality of nations he ruled all round him with the absolutism of a Turkish Sultan.

His tyranny and spirit of discord eventually alienated him from his family, from most of his friends, and from several countries.

Krush, under saddle

Berk (Seyal—Bukra)

Exiled from Egypt, warned against landing in India, and failing in health, he settled down at Newbuildings; but he was of the restless temperament to whom agitation and disturbance are the breath of life, and deprived of political outlet, which had served as a partial safety-valve to his family, his whole concentrated energy was turned against his immediate surroundings.

In 1904 Mr. Blunt made over the Crabbet Estates to his daughter, by Marriage Settlement under Trust. He had first come to live at Newbuildings Place – another of the Blunt properties – in 1871. He succeeded to Crabbet Park upon the death of his brother Francis in 1872, but later returned to Newbuildings where he continued to live until his death in 1922.

Rasim (Feysul—Risala) In 1906 the Blunts finally parted; he to live at Newbuildings whileL ady Anne remained at Crabbet.

Of the 126 horses then at Crabbet, Mr. Blunt took 68. Certain agreements were entered into by him regarding the interchange of stallions and the preservation of foundation stock.

Unfortunately Mr. Blunt did not keep his undertaking, nor did he appear to think he was bound by his agreement in the maintenance of the Stud. The condition of his horses deteriorated through lack of care and bad management. Doubtless, because of disappointment in their resultant looks and performance he sold some for less than they were worth and even gave some away. When an opportunity occurred, as it did occasionally, Lady Anne bought some back.

Bad as conditions had been at Newbuildings they were made far worse by the outbreak of war in 1914. An immediate shortage of male labour could not but affect all farming operations, and care of stock. Food was in short supply; skilled help for the making of hay and the maintenance of buildings was almost impossible to get; horses of the right type were being commandeered by the War Office for the use of Cavalry; and these conditions sounded the death-knell for many Studs.

Mr. Blunt appears to have abandoned all ideas of maintaining his, and what remained of his stock was acquired by his wife, and returned to Crabbet Park.

In 1915, having made provision for the safety and care of her horses in the foreseeable future, Lady Anne returned to her home in Egypt to find peace and balm for her hurt spirit. Lady Wentworth in *The Authentic Arabian Horse*:

> The desert attracted her with irresistible force. Its vast silences, its immense heaven of moon and stars and the mystery of its phantom lakes and waves of mirage, those glorious illusions of reflected skies and ghostly palm-trees in glittering, shimmering waters of incredible reality, and yet more incredible unreality. The golden flood of dawn, the flaming blue and gold of noon, the fairy cloud-shadows blown across immeasurable tracts of plain and valley, and the ever-changing and receding loveliness of its 'Eternal Hills'.
>
> Riding all the day long under a cloudless sky and camping in the blaze of crimson sunset passing into the deep mystery of the desert night. This was her enchanted life of dreams.

She lived now with her dreams, in peace. Though age had crept upon her, her unconquerable spirit left her the enjoyment of those things which delighted her mind; writing and the trust of friendship.

Much of what she wrote in these last few years is of permanent value to the historian.

In December 1917, a month before her eightieth birthday, Lady Anne Blunt fell ill and died, alone. The news of her illness had never reached her family. Whether through the exigencies of war which was then at its darkest period and made communication unsure, or whether the urgency of the message was misunderstood, it is difficult and somewhat meaningless to prove.

Her body was buried where her heart always lived. The Noble Lady of the Horses lies in a tomb still revered by the people of the land which gave her peace.

Following the death of Lady Anne, the Crabbet Stud with its horses of priceless blood, a monument to her life's work which had been acquired and established at a cost of nearly £1,000,000 sterling was in danger of disintegration for an unexpected and incalculable reason. In 1918 the Sheykh Obeyd Stud was dispersed, the major part being purchased by Capt. Trouncer for the Egyptian Horsebreeding Commission.

Before her death Lady Anne Blunt presented the stallion Jamil, a Seglawi Jedran, and the mares Bint Yemama (Yashmak) and Jamila (Jemla) among others to the Egyptian Agricultural Stud.

In the sad closing years of her life, Lady Anne had made a Will leaving her entire Stud and a large part of her estate to her two grand-daughters, the children of her only child, Lady Wentworth. They were both minors and neither of them

Lady Anne Blunt in Arab costume

could be expected to have the knowledge or the resources needed to maintain the Stud at this juncture.

The only person at that time to whom the Stud could have been entrusted was Lady Anne's daughter, Lady Wentworth, who had been completely overlooked in the disposition of the horses.

Complications, almost disastrous to the future of the Stud arose from clauses dealing with the distribution of property which enabled Mr. Blunt to sell the Egyptian establishment at Sheik Obeyd, and the horses that still remained there. Several of these were bought by the Egyptian Government.

Before Lady Anne's Will could be proved, however, Mr. Blunt claimed the Crabbet Park horses as his by right of a previous 'settlement'. Apparently acting on the belief that 'deeds are mightier than words' he organized a raid one night, in the Arab tradition, and forcibly removing all the horses from the stables he carried them off to Newbuildings.

The inevitable result was a lawsuit which dragged on for four years between Mr. Blunt, and the Public Trustee acting on behalf of the grand-children for the recovery of their property.

During the time when the lawsuit was in progress, Lady Wentworth, helpless to protect her children's rights or her mother's legacy, witnessed the sale by her father of valuable horses to anyone willing to pay the price he asked.

Blunt lost his case and following a County Injunction the horses he had taken were returned.

Wilfrid Blunt was now an old and tired man. In the closing chapter of his Diary he writes:

A black melancholy is on me caused by a sense of my failure everywhere in life. My poetry, my Eastern politics, my Arab horse breeding, were strings to my bow and they have one after another snapped.

And again:

I am entering on my eightieth year this month, August 1919, and shall make no further venturings in my lifetime with publicity.

He was reconciled with his family before his death two years later.

His grave is in a Sussex wood in the grounds of the Newbuildings estate. It is encircled by great beech trees through which the light filters in soft green and grey, and where in summer the nightingales sing both night and day.

These words are carved on his grave; a quotation from one of his later poems:

Dear checker-work of woods, the Sussex Weald
If a name thrills me yet of things of earth, That name is thine!
How often have I fled to thy deep hedgerows and embraced each field, each lag*, each
  pasture,
Fields which gave me birth. And saw my youth, and which must hold me dead.

Earliest entries in the special section for Arabians in
Vol. 14 of the General Stud Book

BASILISK

A White Mare, foaled in 1875, a Seglwieh Obeyran of Ibn Ed Derri, her dam stolen from the Ibn Ed Derri family by Faris Assaat, who sold her to Abd el Jadir, of Deyr, in whose possession she was foaled. She was purchased of Abd el Jadir in 1878 for Mr. Blunt.

General Stud Book – Volume 14.

HAGAR

A Bay Mare, foaled in 1872, a Kehilet Ajuz, purchased at Aleppo from an Arab of the Moali, who had recently brought her from the Roala, who had taken her in war from the Sebaa (Anazeh). She was stated to have been bred by Suleyman Jelalah of that tribe – sire same strain of blood.

General Stud Book – Volume 14.

JERBOA

A Bay Mare, foaled in 1874, a Managhieh Hedruj, bred in Deyr, out of a mare from the Obeyd tribe, sire, a Managhi of the Ibn Sbeyel strain, purchased at Deyr, in 1878.

General Stud Book – Volume 14.

KARS

A Bay Colt, foaled in 1874, a Seglawi Jedran of Ibn Sbeni, purchased at Aleppo, from Mahmud Aga, a Kurdish Chief of Irregulars, who obtained him as a two-year-old from the Fedaan-Anazeh, and rode him in 1877 to the war in Armenia, where nearly every other horse perished. His sire is stated to have been of the same strain of blood. This is considered the best in the Syrian Desert.

General Stud Book – Volume 14.

PHAROAH

A Bay Colt, foaled in 1876, a Seglawi Obeyran of Ibn Ed Derri, purchased from Neddi Ibn Ed Derri, of the Resallin (Sebaa Anazeh), his sire, a Kehilan Ajuz, of the Gomussa (Sebaa Anazeh), his dam's sire, a Seglawi Jedran, of Obeyd el Belasi,

* Lag. Old Sussex name for marsh-land.

of the Roala. This strain of blood is considered the best now remaining to the Sebaa. Purchased by Mr. Skene, H.M. Consul at Aleppo, for Mr. Blunt.

General Stud Book – Volume 14.

QUEEN OF SHEBA
A Brown Mare, foaled in 1875, an Abeyeh Sherrak, bred by Erheyen Ibn Alian, of the Gomussa (Seba Anazeh) – her sire a Managhy Hedruj, of Ibn Gufeyfi (Gomussa), purchased of Beteyen Ibn Mirshid Sheykh of the Gomussa, who owned her on shares with her breeder. A celebrated mare. Imported by Mr. Blunt in 1879.

General Stud Book – Volume 14.

RODANIA
A Chestnut Mare, foaled about 1869, a Kehilet Ajuz, bred by Ibn Rodan, of the Roala, and captured from Sotamm Ibn Shaalan, Sheykh of the Roala in 1880, by Tais Ibn Sharban, of the Gomussa (Sebaa Anazeh), who sold her to Mr. Blunt. An old and celebrated mare, formerly the property of Beneyeh Ibn Shaalan, and the cause of a feud between him and his kinsman Sotamm.

General Stud Book – Volume 14.

SHERIFA
A White Mare, foaled about 1862, a Hamdanyeh Simri, bred in Nejd. This mare was presented by Saoud Ibn Saoud, Emir of Riad, to Takeddin Pasha, Governor of Mecca, and by him, who brought her to Aleppo, to Sheykh Takha, Chief Ulema of that town, on whose death, in 1878, she was purchased of his executors for Mr. Blunt.

General Stud Book – Volume 14.

WILD THYME
A Bay Mare, foaled in 1876, said to be a Kehileh Ras el Fedawi, bred by the Baggara tribe of the Euphrates, and purchased of them by Mr. Skene, H.M. Consul at Aleppo, for Mr. Blunt.

General Stud Book – Volume 14.

DAJANIA
A Bay Mare, foaled in 1876, a Kehileh Dajani, bred by Mohammed Pasha, a Turcoman Chief, who stole her dam from the Sebaa (Anazeh), her sire, a Kehilan Nowag. Dajania was in her turn stolen from her owner, and sold to Mr. Blunt, at Aleppo, in 1877.

General Stud Book – Volume 15.

HADBAN

Foaled in 1878, a Hadban Enzeyhi, bred by Jakin Ibn Akil, Sheykh of the Daajeyni tribe of Ateybah, a tribe of Western Nejd, who sold him as a five-year-old to Ali Ibn Amr of Bussora, who brought him to Bombay, where he was purchased by Mr. Blunt in 1884, and imported into England that year.

General Stud Book – Volume 15.

AZREK

Foaled in 1881, a Grey Horse, of the Seglawi Jedran breed of Ibn el Derri, bred by Sheykh Mashlab Ibn ed Derri, of the Gomussa tribe of Sebaa Anazeh, purchased from the breeder by Mr. Blunt in 1887, in the desert of Northern Arabia, and imported in the spring of 1888. A celebrated stallion.

General Stud Book – Volume 16.

MERZUK

A Chestnut Horse, foaled in 1887, a Kehilan Jellabieh, bred by Ali Pasha Sherif, dam, a Kehilet Jellabieh, sire, Wazir, the celebrated Seglawi Jedran of Ibn Sudan's strain. Imported by Mr. Blunt in 1891, and sent the same year to the Cape, after covering in this country.

General Stud Book – Volume 17.

MESAOUD

A Chestnut Horse, foaled in 1887, a Seglawi Jedran of Ibn Sudan's strain. Bred by Ali Pasha Sherif, dam, Yemama, a Seglawieh Jedran of the Ibn Sudan's strain, sire, Aziz, a Dahman Shahwan. Imported by Mr. Blunt in 1891.

General Stud Book – Volume 17.

SOBHA

A White Mare, foaled in 1879, by Hamdanieh Simri, purchased by Mr. W. S. Blunt from her breeder, Mahmud Bey, and imported in 1891; her dam, the Hamdanieh Simri, purchased by Mahmud Bey at the sale of Abbas Pasha's Stud; her sire, Wazir, the celebrated Seglawi Jedran of Ibn Sudan's strain, bred by Ali Pasha Sherif.

General Stud Book – Volume 17.

FERIDA

A Bay Mare, foaled in 1886, imported in 1891, a Managhieh Hedruzieh, purchased by Mr. W. S. Blunt from Khuddr Jemal ed Din, who brought her from Deyr on the Euphrates.

General Stud Book – Volume 18.

BINT NURA

A Chestnut Mare, foaled about 1885, a Dahmeh Nejib, bred by the late Ali Pasha Sherif, in Cairo, both sire and dam of strains from the stud collected by Abbas I, Viceroy of Egypt, imported in 1897.

General Stud Book – Volume 19.

FEYSUL

A Kehilan Ajuz, of the Jellabi strain, or Kahilan Jellabi, a Chestnut Horse (off-hind foot white and narrow blaze), foaled in 1894, bred by the late Ali Pasha Sherif, in Cairo, his dam, a Kehileh Jellabieh, whose grandam was purchased by Abbas Pasha I, Viceroy of Egypt, from Feysul Ibn Turki, Emir of Riad, who had her from Ibn Khalifeh, Sheykh of Bahreyn, possessor of that strain from the Ajman tribe of Eastern Nejd, his sire, Ibn Nura, a Dahman Nejib, a white fleabitten horse. Both sire and dam bred by Ali Pasha Sherif, and descended from horses and mares brought from Arabia to Egypt by Abbas Pasha I, Viceroy of Egypt. Purchased after the death of Ali Pasha Sherif. Imported by Mr. Blunt from Sheykh Obeyd Stud in Egypt, in September, 1904.

General Stud Book – Volume 19.

MAHRUSS

A Chestnut, foaled in 1893, a Dahman Nejib, bred by the late Ali Pasha Sherif in Cairo, dam, Bint Nura, a Dahmeh Nejib, sire, Mahrus, a Wadnan Hursan, both sire and dam from strains from the stud collected by Abbas Pasha I, Viceroy of Egypt, imported by Mr. Blunt in 1897.

General Stud Book – Volume 19.

The following horses imported into the Crabbet Stud are descended from both sides from the 'ABBAS PASHA the 1st' collection, without admixture:

SOBHA	1879	KALALLA	1895
SAFRA	1885	KHAMSA	1897
KHATILA	1887	JALMUDA	1898
SEFINA	1892	FADILA	1898
BINT HELWA	1887	MESAOUD	1887
JOHARA	1880	MERZUK	1887
FULANA	1893	SHAHWAN	1887
BADIA	1884	MAHRUSS	1893
BINT NURA	1885	SAFRAN	1893
MAKBULA	1886	ABU KHASHEB	1894
JELLABIEH	1892	DAOUD	1899
KASIDA	1891		

Chapter 4

Days of Glory

FROM THIS fateful beginning, the next step in a pilgrimage which began in the desert, succeeding years would witness the rise of the most brilliant galaxy of Arabian horses that the contemporary world had seen.

The Stud of Arabians at Crabbet Park, or to give it its historic title, the Crabbet Arabian Stud, had to be reconstituted when it became the property of Lady Wentworth. This was not an easy task, since so much of the precious foundation stock had suffered from neglect in the years preceding her absolute ownership, and showed the effects of this neglect, particularly in the young ones and brood mares.

The Stud's economic stability too had been seriously shaken, and like many another breeder in the same predicament, Lady Wentworth was faced with the decision of choosing the best of the breeding stock and selling the others until such time as the Stud could be made economically sound.

The evidence of her attention to the well-being and the restoration of the Stud Farm was soon apparent in the increase of size and substance of the Crabbet horses. This, added to their inherited beauty and high-born 'presence' brought ever-increasing admiration, both at home and abroad for the 'Crabbet Arabians'.

The mature stallions of note inherited by Lady Wentworth when the horses returned to Crabbet Park, were, Daoud, Nasik, Ibn Yashmak, Rafeef, Nureddin, Hazzam and Raswan.

Of mares, the most outstanding were Ferda, Fejr, Nasra, Nisreen, Nashisha, Nasira, Nessima, Selma, Risala, Rish, Rissla, Marhaba, Somra, and their foals.

In 1918 the Arab Horse Society was founded, through the enthusiasm and energy of Mr. H. V. Musgrave Clark, Mr. Sidney Hough, Mr. George Ruxton, and the Rev. D. B. Montefiore.

Their effort received the support of a surprising number of people who, either bred Arabs, appreciated them as hacks, or had owned them in the East and in many instances brought them home.

The first Stud Book of the Society, under the patronage of H.M. The King of Iraq, was published in 1919.

It lists 148 members; one of whom is Col. T. E. Lawrence, C.B., D.S.O. of the Emir Faisal's Staff, Damascus.

Breeders and owners, numbering thirty-five, are listed separately, headed by H.M. The King, H.R.H. the Prince of Wales, and H.H. the King of the Hedjaz.

Mares at Crabbet Park, left to right: Riyala, Rythma, Nasra and Rissala

Ferhan (Raswan—Fejr)

One hundred horses are registered, several from abroad, but the greater number are either owned by the Blunts, or had been purchased from them.

Up to this time there were no breed classes for Arabs at any of the Shows. The National Pony Societies' Show at Hurlingham and at the Agricultural Hall, Islington, provided classes for Eastern horses, which of course could include Barbs, or any other 'Eastern' variety. Later, there were classes for pure Arabians at Ranelagh, Newmarket, and Richmond, though at these early shows 'the Arab breed' might be represented by no more than nine individuals. But the number of breeders and support for the Society continued to increase till the outbreak of the Second World War in 1939.

In the year 1920 a hallmark of distinction was set upon the Crabbet Stud, and the unique genius of Lady Wentworth demonstrated by her purchase of Skowronek. This stallion was to be a kind of talisman of success for Crabbet.

If Fate governs the lives of horses it could not be more clearly demonstrated than in the life of Skowronek. He was sold from Count Potockis' Stud in Poland to Mr. Walter Winans, a hackney-breeder who brought him to England in 1913.

Within a year he was sold again to Mr. Webb-Ware who used him as a hack

Rafeef (Nasik—Riyala)

*Hazzam
(Berk—Hilmyeh)*

Skowronek

throughout the Great War, and was the first owner to appreciate his beauty, but did not use him for breeding. In 1919 he was again for sale and Mr. H. V. Musgrave Clark bought him but used him very little, perhaps because it was war-time.

In 1920, Lady Wentworth saw Skowronek, and recognizing his perfect type she bought him, little realizing that the fame of her Stud would be forever associated with his name, and that the influence of his blood would be seen and acclaimed in every country that recognizes the value of Arab-breeding today.

The next fortuitous circumstance that was to be of immeasurable value to the Crabbet Stud was the establishment of another Stud in 1925 by Lady Yule and her daughter, Gladys Yule. Lady Yule had spent much of her life in India where she had been attracted by the Arabians seen on the Calcutta race-course, though her chief interest was in Thoroughbreds. After the death of her husband she made her home at Hanstead House, a mansion standing in a beautiful estate in Hertfordshire, and designed a model Stud Farm which could not have been surpassed for elegance anywhere in the world. It was the most perfect setting for Arabian horses, as well as for Thoroughbreds. By a happy coincidence it was at this time that Lady Wentworth was selling some of her good stock and Lady Yule, who had enough experience and knowledge to choose the best, bought the mare Razina, by Rasim ex Riyala, who was to earn fame as one of the best brood mares of all time; Astrella (Raseem—Amida), one of the few classically-bred Abeyieh Sherrakieh mares left in England; the Skowronek daughter, Naxina out of Nessima; and Niseyra, perhaps the finest daughter of Rissam, out of Neraida.

She also bought the stallion Rissalix, whose get was to have such an important influence on the future of Arab breeding.

Lady Yule had for some years an arrangement of mutual pre-emption of stock with Lady Wentworth; the main object was to consolidate and extend the Crabbet blood concentration, and this arrangement continued through the years of the Second World War.

Another Stud which added lustre to the history of these days was that of Mr. H. V. Musgrave Clark, owner of the Courthouse Stud in Sussex, and one of the founders of the Arab Horse Society. Established in 1900, it has remained in the one ownership which justifies its claim to be the second oldest Arabian Stud in England.

Mr. Clark was in his youth a fine horseman, a lover and connoisseur of the Arabian horse, and a friend of Lady Anne Blunt from whom he learnt much that was to help him in the future. Four foundation mares were purchased from the Blunts.

They were:

Feluka (Messaoud—Ferida); this mare was the dam of the beautiful Fasiha, by Skowronek.

Balis (Seyal—Bukra).

Raseem (Rasim—Rim)

Shareer (Nureddin II—Selima)

Belkis (Seyal—Bereyda); and Jellabieh, an imported Kehaileh Ajuz bred by Ibn Khalifah, Sheikh of Bahrein.

Three good stallions from Crabbet were added to the Stud. They were: Rodan (Rijm—Rakima); Mustapha Kamel (Feysul—Mabsuta); and Mansur (Daoud—Mabsuta). Later, the mares Nessima (Rijm—Narghileh), and Belka (Rijm—Bereyda) were purchased. In 1919 Skowronek was bought but used so sparingly that there is only one line of Skowronek blood in the Stud today.

Mr. Clark in his search for the perfect type of history, also added to his Stud several years later three desert-bred stallions, Nimr, Atesh, and Fedaan. Lady Wentworth's gift to Mrs. Musgrave Clark, was the Crabbet mare Safarjal, who was in foal to Rasim. The colt born subsequently was Sanfoin, who with Champurrado could justly be appraised as two of the most influential stallions at Courthouse. Both are of pure Abbas Pasha—Blunt blood. Champurrado (Irex—Niseyra) was bred by the late Lady Yule at Hanstead, and is the sole representative of the Skowronek line at Courthouse. Mr. Musgrave Clark's own assessment of the best of his horses that are of Abbas Pasha-Blunt breeding are: among the foundation mares; Balis (Seyal—Bukra), Belka (Rijm—Bereyda), Feluka (Mesaoud—Ferida), Nessima (Rijm—Narghileh), Rangha (Berk—Rabla), and Rahab (Sanfoin—Rangha). Of the stallions bred at Courthouse: Sanfoin, Rheoboam (Sanfoin—Rangha), Razaz (Champurrado—Rahab), Shammar (Champurrado—Somra), and Bahram (Sanfoin—Bettina), a horse, who perfectly demonstrated the classic beauty of the Arabian.

Mirage, Desert bred; a Kehailan Ajuz

In 1966 the Stud consisted of eight stallions and twenty mares; a comparatively small band of horses; yet Mr. Clark's genius had achieved a uniformity of type, conformation, and above all classic beauty which could have enriched Arabian stock in many countries. Unfortunately, breeding within the Stud was on a restricted scale, and very seldom was an outside mare accepted. Thus a brilliant assembly of stallions and mares are represented outside the Stud by very few individuals.

In Australia, Razaz (Champurrado—Rahab by Sanfoin ex Rangha), and in America, Nimrod (Champurrado—Nautch Girl, by Sanfoin ex Nasira) will be remembered as classic sires.

During the years of disaster, 1939–1945, every form of horse-breeding was curtailed to such an extent that many Studs had to give up altogether.

All but the minimum of grazing land was requisitioned; no corn could be obtained except a ration for breeding stock entered in the General Stud Book, and labour was practically unobtainable.

The two Studs on which the survival of Arabian breeding now depended, Crabbet Park and Hanstead, were by reason of their favourable circumstances able to continue increasing their stock, but on a restricted scale.

Hanstead, using Crabbet stallions, bred Raktha, by Naseem, out of Razina. Grey Owl by Raseem, out of Naxina. Riffal by Naufal, out of Razina, and the three beautiful mares, Shamnar, by Naziri out of Razina; Sulka by Naseem, and Queen Zenobia (Radi—Sulka). Rissam was there on lease and was the sire of Carlina, out of Shamnar.

Crabbet Park had at the time a wonderful array of brood mares, and the fine stallions Raseem, Naziri, Naufal, Indian Gold, Faris, and Radi.

No doubt because of the success of the outcross of Skowronek blood, a second stallion of desert breeding was acquired from King Faisal of Irak.

This was Mirage. He was imported by King Faisal from the Denadsha tribe, through General Haddad Pasha, who identified the horse and his history. Mirage was a Kehailan Ajuz of the Denadsha strain. Though greatly admired, he was not used in the Crabbet Stud and was eventually sold to Roger A. Selby of Portsmouth, Ohio, as fortunate a circumstance for the Selby Stud as the advent of Skowronek had been for Crabbet.

Just before the outbreak of war Lady Wentworth sold thirty horses, including the Supreme Champions Naseem and Shareer to Russia, as foundation stock for their Government Stud. It is highly improbable that she would have done this could she have foreseen the future.

As the war dragged on with its uncertainties of survival, and with Arab breeding in England reduced to a minimum, there were not enough replacements for the older mares and stallions of Abbas Pasha—Blunt blood, now almost exclusively centred in the Hanstead and Crabbet Studs. In honour of their mutual agreement,

Silver Fire
(Naseem—Somra)

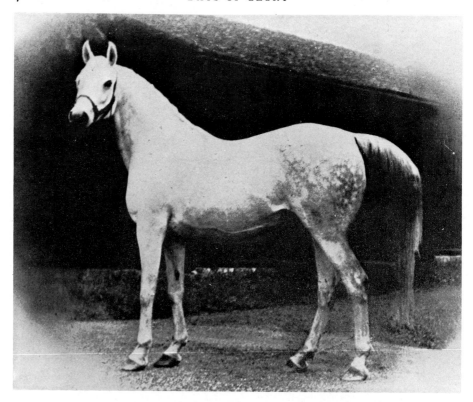

Neraida
(Nureddin II—Nasifa)

Raktha
(Naseem—Razina)

Naseem
(Skowronek—Nasra)

Raktha, Naseem's best son was given to Crabbet, a valuable acquisition as the future would prove.

Shortly after, Lady Yule withdrew from her agreement with Lady Wentworth concerning the exchange of stock and transferred the ownership of her Stud to her daughter, Miss Gladys Yule.

Export was made impossible by the dangers of travel by sea, and many valuable young colts were of necessity sold to circuses, to riding-schools as hacks, or to run with pony herds.

One such colt was Oran, an Abeyan Sherrakh by Riffal out of Astrella, bred at Hanstead. He had been sold to a small Stud-owner who apparently did not recognise his potential value and offered him for sale again. Lady Wentworth then bought him, and in a few years both Raktha and Oran established themselves as the leading sires of the Crabbet Stud.

Not the least of the catastrophic consequences of the enforced limitation of breeding during the war years was the fact that many of the finest stallions were in their prime, yet could not be used. What would we not have given for more sons and daughters of Rissam, Naufal, Indian Gold and Naziri, for example?

At the Hanstead Stud, horses of excellence to match those of Crabbet were being bred. Denied the use of Crabbet stallions after the break in their friendly

Rissalix
(Faris—Rissla)

relations, Lady Yule used Algol (Dwarka—Rythama), to produce the fine mare Namilla, out of Razina. Nuri Sherif (Nureddin—Sheeba) sired the beautiful Nurschida out of Razina. Nurschida was the dam of Rikitea, by Rissalix.

The young Serafix (Raktha—Serafina)

General Grant, a son of Raktha was now also used as a younger stallion, though the senior stallion was still Rissalix (Faris—Rissla), a chestnut horse of superb quality. As a sire of distinction it would be difficult to find his equal. His sons became noted for their marvellous action and classic excellence as well as their ability to pass on that excellence to their progeny.

It should be recorded here, that in spite of the critical times, the War Office gave special consideration to the preservation of the Arabian. An article which appeared in the magazine *Riding* in November, 1939,* illustrates this:

THE ARAB HORSE AND THE WAR OFFICE

The War Office has given instructions to all purchasing officers in the various Army Commands that no Arab horses are to be purchased or impressed for

* By courtesy of *Riding*.

Army Service. We understand that these instructions were issued as the result of representations made by the Arab Horse Society's Secretary, Brig. Gen. W. H. Anderson, C.B.E., to whom the thanks of all owners of Arab horses are due. The demand for Arabian horses and their scarcity is such that their exclusion from purchase by the Army is very welcome.

In point of fact, the future of the Arabian horse needs careful consideration. As we have remarked elsewhere in this issue, there is a great reduction in the breeding of high-caste Arabians in Arabia. Moreover, the Spanish Civil War caused the dispersal of several famous Studs. Now the misfortunes of Poland have resulted in the destruction of many of the best Studs of Arabian horses in the world. When peace returns to Europe the Arab blood will be in even greater demand than it is now. It is hoped that Arab breeders in this country will maintain their Studs during the war so far as they possibly can. They will reap their reward later.

This policy was certainly justified within the next few years.

The end of the War in 1945 saw a period of reconstruction and a fresh appraisal of values in England. So much had been lost of beauty and worth, so much that

Bahram
(Sainfoin—Bettina)

was old and precious had been destroyed. Both mentally and physically there was a desire to build afresh. The State helped to restore war-damaged homes and buildings; land requisitioned was gradually given back to the owners, and people began to think once more of the cultivation of beauty where they had been forced for six years to consider only utility.

An extraordinary revival of interest in Arabians was a symptom of the times. As may be imagined there were very few for sale; fewer still were the really good specimens available. Studs that had survived the difficult years were unwilling to part with their best stock at any price.

In 1946 the first two All Arabian Shows were held. A Spring and a Summer Show. People who knew little about Arabs, came out of curiosity to see either 'something out of a picture-book' or an undersized 'pony-type' horse, and though the classes were by no means big it was impressive enough as a spectacle to bring such a large crowd to the Summer Show that the printed Schedules fell short of the number required, and the ring was too small to accommodate the crowd of spectators round it. Though several Studs were represented, the winning horses with four exceptions came from either Crabbet or the Hanstead Studs.

It was here that the author saw, for the first time, Grey Royal, that exquisite daughter of Raktha. The entries in the class had been lined up by the judges; a class which included Rubiana, Carlina and Selma II, all beautiful fillies who drew murmurs of admiration from the crowd, and then, suddenly making a late entrance, Grey Royal 'floated' in. There was an amazed hush in the crowd. The arch of her neck, the carriage of her tail, and her airy, almost weightless action were incredible. Together with her perfectly dappled coat, and dark mane and tail, she made a picture that must always live in the memory.

Grey Royal won the class, and was never beaten in her show career though she met all the best mares in the country.

The next ten years saw the founding of many new Arabian Studs, and the rebuilding and expansion of several old-established ones.

The Hanstead Stud using Rissalix (bred at Crabbet), Grey Owl (bred at Hanstead), Radi (bred by Mrs. Carrol in Ireland), and Riffal of Hanstead breeding, produced a succession of horses whose names will go down in Arabian history for their singular beauty and the influence they have had on future generations. The stallions Blue Domino, Count Dorsaz, Mikeno and General Grant alone would have made this Stud famous without including any of the mares who have added so much to the value of Arabians today.

The genius of Lady Wentworth could not be better demonstrated than by a study of her work after the War was over. Her knowledge of the value of certain blood-lines, and the ultimate result of breeding and cross-breeding of individuals;

Irex (Naseem—Rissla)

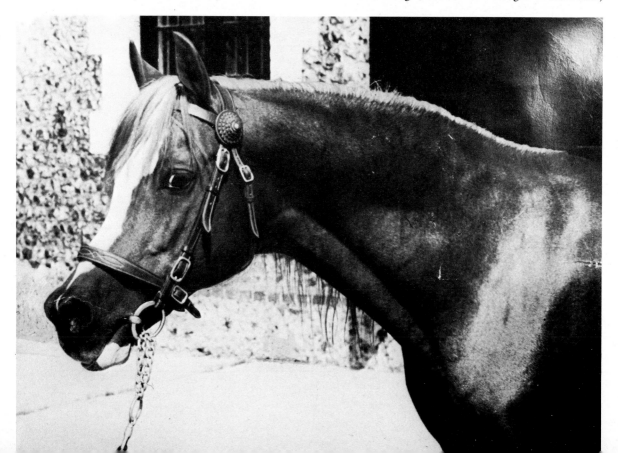

her almost infallible judgement of the future excellence of a colt; and her insistence that an even greater approach to perfection could be achieved in the Arab of the future. These qualities, besides the incomparable experience provided by the circumstances of her life, in seeing and appraising the best types of Arabians since childhood, and in hearing the considered judgement of her parents, must have given her a kind of inborn knowledge which would have been impossible for her to convey to others. Her work, a continuation of that done by Lady Anne Blunt and Wilfrid Scawen Blunt has made the Crabbet Stud the most famous foundation Stud in the world.

To list the honours won by stock bred at the Crabbet would demand a book. Their successes are world-wide, and it may be taken for granted that where there is excellence there is Crabbet blood, if not in that generation then certainly in the preceding ones.

To quote the Show Successes in any one year. At home in 1950 there were:

13 Championships
 9 Reserve Championships
26 Firsts
 1 Supreme Horse of the Year Championship
 1 Reserve Supreme Horse of the Year Championship
 8 Cups
 7 Medals.

In succeeding years Arabians bred at other Studs challenged the supremacy of the Crabbet stock. Gladys Yule, a most generous and far-seeing woman who cared for the future of the Arabian as much as for her own successes, would never refuse an outside mare to her stallions to help new breeders, and would sell a good filly if she were satisfied that it would be valued as such. Breeders of the present day in England owe her a debt that can never be repaid.

With few exceptions the three great Studs of Crabbet, Hanstead and Court-house dominated the breeding classes at shows.

While the Hanstead and Courthouse horses were smaller and more classic in type, the Crabbet horses had presence, quality, and a regal bearing that has never been equalled. A horse like Raktha, or his son Indian Magic outshone everything at a Show, with their pride of carriage. Having looked at them once the eye constantly returned for the joy of looking again at a perfect work of art.

Grand Royal was a majestic horse, and the young Serafix and Royal Crystal could best be described as models, the one in bronze and the other in black onyx.

Mares like Grey Royal, Shades of Night, Crown Royal and Silver Shadow could seldom have been surpassed in stately beauty.

Horses of Crabbet blood had certain features which set them apart; they were

Oran (Riffal—Astrella)

taller than their contemporaries, they had wonderfully free action, good shoulders, and were noticeable for the perfect angle at which the head was set.

A distinguished visitor from the East, El Hami el Mansoor, after a visit to the Crabbet Stud wrote:

All the young ones seem to be increasing in size at much the same average speed every year. The Silver Fire and Oran lines are specially stamped with gazelle heads and all the stock is noticeable for the 'jibba' and 'Mitbakh', traditions in the desert blood. This exquisite setting of neck (particularly seen in Silver Shadow, Indian Gold, Sharima, Grey Royal, Sun Royal, and Crown Royal) was one of the beautiful points of Bint Nura, dam of Daoud, and descends to many of her produce through Champions Nasra and Naseem, reinforced by the Skowronek arch of neck in later days.

OPPOSITE PAGE

(above) *Count Dorsaz (Rissalix—Shamnar)*

(below) *Silver Vanity (Oran—Silver Gilt)*

General Grant
(Raktha—Samsie)

These were the days of glory for Arabians in England. Membership of the Arab Horse Society increased rapidly, and the merits of the Arabian as a riding horse were for the first time brought to the notice of the general English horse-loving world. Miss Yule made a point of training her Arab stallions for performance, and at the White City International Show, the Winston Churchill Cup for the best riding horse of the year of all breeds was twice awarded to her Count Dorsaz, and once to his son Count Orlando. Some of the finest Anglo-Arabs were also bred at Hanstead and ridden to win prizes in open competition as Show Hacks. The Arabian Show at Roehampton became a social function attended by Royalty, and in 1956 graced by the presence of Her Majesty the Queen.

Then in 1957 came unforeseen disaster. Lady Wentworth and Miss Gladys Yule died within a month of each other – and the disposition of their Studs became a matter of urgency for which no one had a ready solution. Miss Yule was extremely wealthy, and Lady Wentworth's estate was of considerable value so that the death duties payable to the State could not be met except by the sale of a large part of the assets, which included the two valuable Studs.

It seemed inevitable that this great company of horses, these travellers from the desert who were of one blood would now be separated.

Chapter 5

Al-Marah

IT SOON became known that the two great breeding establishments of Crabbet Park and Hanstead House would have to be drastically reduced.

No single British breeder at that time could afford to acquire either Stud, as a whole. They represented the cream of the breeding stock in England and their value in terms of money would represent a fortune.

In retrospect it seems that there could have been no alternative to the distribution of the horses, perhaps at home, and most certainly abroad.

Then once more, Fate played a part and their unity was saved.

One of the most dedicated breeders of Arabians and the owner of the largest privately-owned Stud in the world is Mrs. Garvin Tankersley. Her Al-Marah Stud in America at that time housed 200 horses, of which at least seventy-five per cent were of Crabbet blood.

Mrs. Tankersley had the advantage of considerable wealth, and the even greater advantage for a breeder, of imagination and experience, and an unrivalled knowledge of bloodlines. She had an intuitive conviction that if the band of Arabian horses which had been preserved intact for a century should now be dispersed, the entire world would lose the treasure of this priceless blood. It was imperative that they should be kept together. She sent three representatives to England to find out which horses were for sale, assess their value and arrange for their transport to her Stud in Maryland.

In the winter of 1957 an importation to America as significant in Arabian history as that made by the Blunts to England, was the landing at Al-Marah Farm of thirteen mares and five stallions from Crabbet Park, and thirteen mares and one stallion from Hanstead House.

Today there are at Al-Marah 153 Senior Mares of whom thirty-six are of pure Abbas Pasha-Blunt bloodlines, and the rest have fifty to ninety-six percent of this blood.

Al-Marah, which means in Arabic 'a green place' was founded in 1939, but the foundation stone had been laid many years before in a young girl's search for her ideal. The girl was Bazy McCormick and in her own words this is how it all began:

The nameless longing in every soul does not always know for what it hungers. When a dream does take shape the person is blest who can find the tangible object of the dream. To many of us an Arabian horse is the fulfilment of our

dream; not just any Arabian horse but the one who epitomizes those qualities
we long to behold. Indraff was my dream without my knowing it, and in the
mysterious way of life he was born the year he took shape in my imagination,
though I did not find him till 8 years later. The three-quarter Arabian mare
given me by my Mother as a child, inspired my yearning for a 'perfect' Arabian
horse. 'Little Jo', was the prettiest, toughest, most affectionate pony I had ever
known. When she died of sleeping sickness I was inconsolable. I did not want
to replace her because to me there could never be another 'Little Jo'.

I was 16, and began to read about Arabians and write letters to W. R. Brown
and Albert Harris and look at pictures. I can't remember now if I had a picture
in my mind of the Arabian stallion that I wanted. I only know that I looked at
what seemed like hundreds and never considered buying one. Somehow I
didn't want to buy a horse that would satisfy me. I saw many such. I wanted to
wait for the horse that I could never be satisfied without, and when Indraff*
walked out of his stable door my whole aesthetic being went out to him in a
thrill of recognition. To this day, he lives in my memory as the picture of
perfection.

One of the greatest horsewomen I know is Miss Charlotte Nolan, the founder
and head of Foxcroft School. For four years I learned everything I could from
her about horses. In her wisdom I think perhaps she knew that horses were my
life. She told me once that every person who loves horses has but one horse in
his life, that is *the* horse. In a sense this is true, but only in so far as a companion
or as a good ride. With a great sire like Indraff his greatness is measured by his
ability to duplicate himself again and again with only minor variations.

My standard will always be Indraff; my goal to recreate him, for he is my
dream. Like Macbeth's vision of MacDuff in the series of mirrors showing 'sons
following sons forever down the shining years ahead'.

This was the beginning of the great Al-Marah organization. 'Stud' does not
adequately describe the vast activities of this estate of 2,500 acres in Maryland.
The Stud Farm comprises 400 acres. The ranch grazes a herd of Polled Herefords
and Santa Gertrudis cattle; grows feed for the 300 Arabians which now comprise
the Stud; and within its bounds, and connected by fine roads, are scattered the
charming dwellings of the staff employed in the Stud and on the Farm of Mr. and
Mrs. Garvin E. Tankersley.

To return to the history of the horses bred at Al-Marah. The foundation mares
were Selfra (Selmian—Rose of France) bred by Roger Selby and owned by
General Dickinson, Gutne (Bazleyd—Gharifet) dam of Al-Marah Radames; and
Rose of Luzon (Gulastra—Rose of France), bred by J. M. Dickinson and owned
by Bazy Tankersley. Other foundation stock was acquired from the foremost
breeders in the United States at the time. Two mares came from Van Vleet;

* Indraff (Raffles—
Indaia is of pure Crab-
bet blood.

*Selfra
(Selmian—Rose of
France)*

several mares and a stallion were bred at the Selby Stud; and a few choice mares were bought when General Dickinson's Traveller's Rest Stud was dispersed.

Indraff, by the Skowronek son Raffles, out of the Raseem—Nisreen daughter Indaia, was tried with these first mares. Where the results were successful more mares of approximately the same breeding were purchased.

Though the mares brought in the various bloodlines deemed necessary for preserving conformation and type; the blood of Gulastra, Raseyn, Antez, Nasr, and Sulejman for example; there was from the beginning a certain amount of in-breeding to the daughters of Raffles, that is, half-sisters of Indraff.

In 1956, when the Bent River Stud was dispersed, Rapture, a son of Raffles out of a full sister of Indraff was bought to be crossed with Indraff daughters and the mares Mlecha, Cassandra (full sister to Rose-Marie) and her daughter Calla, by Rapture. By 1964 the Al-Marah Stud owned forty-four Indraff daughters of the highest quality.

It had long been felt at Al-Marah that a further outcross was needed which America could not supply. An outcross to complete perfection, a longer neck, higher withers, a finer throat latch and a free stride, and the English imports were the answer to this need.

These horses are important because of their historic lineage and their names are here recorded:

Alicia, gr. f. (Iridos x Salinas)
Blue Millet, ch. m. (Blue Domino x Namilla)
Bright Diamond, ch. c. (Bright Shadow x Silver Diamond)
Crown of Destiny, ch. m. (Oran x Grey Royal)
Crystal Special, ch. c. (Royal Crystal x Extra Special)
Crystal Voyager, ch. c. (Royal Crystal x Nerina)
Grey Stella, gr. m. (Grey Owl x Umatella)

Al-Marah Radames
(Indraff—Gutne)

Indian Diamond, ch. m. (Oran x Indian Flower)
Kabara, ch. m. (Rissalix x Shamnar)
Little Owl, gr. s. (Grey Owl x Kabara)
Lucretia, ch. f. (Count Orlando x Minta)
Minta, ch. m. (Rasham x Wardi)
Nadeyria, ch. m. (Count Dorsaz x Radeyra)
Orsino, gr. c. (Count Orlando x Rafeena)
Radeyra, ch. m. (Radi x Niseyra)
Reenexa, gr. m. (Irex x Rafeena)
Rosalissa, ch. m. (Grey Owl x Rosalina)
Royal Constellation, ch. c. (Grand Royal x Serafina)
Royal Diamond, gr. s. (Oran x Grey Royal)
Salinas, gr. m. (Grey Owl x Shamnar)
Shades of Night, ch. m. (Rissam x Sharfina)
Silver Diamond, ch. m. (Grand Royal x Silver Gilt)

Silver Grand, gr. m. (Grand Royal x Silver Gilt)
Silver Glory, ch. f. (Silver Vanity x Silfina)
Silver Shadow, gr. m. (Oran x Silver Fire)
Silwa, gr. m. (Raktha x Silver Crystal)
Silwara, ch. f. (Dargee x Silwa)
Siyama, ch. m. (Grand Royal x Serafina)
Taheki, ch. m. (Grey Owl x Rikitea)
Thora Grant, ch. m. (General Grant x Thoraya)
Thoraya, b., m. (Rissalix x Samsie)
Zulima, b., m. (Rissalix x Queen Zenobia)

Not yet content with her collection of 'crown jewels' Mrs. Tankersley felt that yet another outcross of a special line was needed. A stallion worthy of Al-Marah's forty-four daughters of Indraff. With an inspiration worthy of genius, she first leased, then purchased from Miss Patricia Wolf, Miss Gladys Yule's heiress in England, the stallion Count Dorsaz. Count Dorsaz by Rissalix out of Shamnar, had twice won the Winston Churchill Cup at the White City in England for the supreme riding Horse. The success of this Count Dorsaz—Indraff cross was spectacular.

By 1966 the brood mare band at Al-Marah had grown to 200. Count Dorsaz was now twenty years old. The sons of Indraff used on Crabbet mares had been entirely successful and now to supplement the blood lines of Count Dorsaz Mrs. Tankersley looked again for a fresh infusion of Crabbet blood, and in partnership with Mr. Charles Prange of New Hope, Pennsylvania, she imported a grey stallion that she had tried unsuccessfully to buy in 1957.

This was the majestic Silver Vanity, of the Hamdani Simri strain, by Oran out of Silver Gilt, one of the finest mares ever bred at Crabbet.

PART 2

Chapter 6

The Legacy

TO ASSESS the influence of the bloodlines today which had their origin in that noble band of horses whose history has here been set out would be a task that could never be completed.

One can follow a great river to its source; its tributaries feed and enrich the earth though they may not all be recorded on any map.

Today, the Arabian horse has stepped out of the pages of legend and history and has accepted a status in our modern world even more demanding than the part he played in his ancient desert life.

Arabians have become international currency, a situation likely to widen in the foreseeable future. Their breeding and study of bloodlines, exact knowledge of conformation and genetics and above all experienced assessment of the subtle qualities which make up the 'asil' Arabian horse, are aspects which require from the individual breeder patient research, courage to accept disappointment, tenacity of purpose, and the two valuable gifts of a good memory, and 'an eye for a horse'.

Because of the international aspect of breeding today it is of greater importance than ever before to have authentic knowledge of the source and direction of the strains, families, and individual horses who have in the past, and still have today, the greatest influence on the betterment of the Arabian breed. No longer do we need legends and travellers tales to support our theories. With the aid of cameras, films, and recorded statistics, it is easy to obtain most of the information we require. Nevertheless, no theories, experience, knowledge, or statistics have yet supplied the formula for breeding perfection.

One incontrovertible fact is recognised wherever Arabians are bred today.

The finest individuals and the most consistently successful lines are those which stem from horses bred at Crabbet Park, which in their turn derive from the Abbas Pasha–Blunt importations whose history has been recorded in the opening chapters.

Today horses of this breeding are renowned, in bloodlines that are regarded as the most valuable, all over the world.

The greatest concentration of this blood is to be found in America, the largest number of horses of pure Crabbet blood being at the Al-Marah Stud Farm in Maryland.

The second largest group of this family of exclusive breeding is in England, still the Mecca of Arabian breeders all over the world. Centuries of horse breeding, horse management, an almost fanatical love of the horse, combined with ideal soil and pasture conditions have transformed the English-bred Arabian in some aspects. They have increased in bone, and in scope, and have demonstrated their versatility, combined with size and elegance. Their popularity not only to 'the Arabian fanatic' but to knowledgeable horsemen, is growing steadily.

Taking advantage of the ease and rapidity of modern travel many owners of Arabian Studs are visiting countries where similar Studs exist, for comparison and appraisal of stock. Though statistics of successful bloodlines or individuals are not available in every country, it is of interest to note how far and how significant has been the influence of those horses of pure Abbas Pasha–Blunt descent.

Chapter 7

Great Britain

THOUGH IN no way comparable to America, numerically or in the extent of the Stud Farms, the British breeder had certain advantages.

The size of the country made it possible to appreciate readily what other breeders were achieving, and to assess, to modify, or indeed to give an entirely new direction to a breeding programme.

The existence of three established Studs of such eminence as Crabbet Park, Hanstead House, and the Courthouse Stud, set a standard of type and an almost automatic directive in breeding which served to uphold a high standard amongst smaller Studs.

Then also the source of good stock, and the services of good stallions, though not freely available, were within the country.

It is important here to note that in 1921, Messrs. Weatherby & Sons, the Keepers of the Stud Book, decided that the same conditions of entry for the General Stud Book must apply to Arabians as for thoroughbred stock. In consequence of this decision no fresh entries were included in the General Stud Book after the issue of Volume 25.

Horses *imported* after this, that is to say, after 1921, were not eligible for entry unless they traced to sires and dams already accepted and entered in earlier Volumes.

This ruling led to the establishment of an elite society of Arabians whose pedigrees were guaranteed by the highest authority, the General Stud Book.

The majority of Arabians entered before 1921 were the Blunt importations, the source of the best blood in British Studs today. But it is of interest to know that of the fifty-three imported Arabians registered in the General Stud Book, that were *not* imported by the Blunts, only four have made any impact worth recording on the pedigrees of the Arabian in Britain today.

Skowronek, not so much an influence, as the founder of a dynasty, is not included in this list. Since his pedigree and history are of international interest they have been dealt with at some length in later pages.

The first of the four is El Emir, whose pedigree has been a matter of controversy. Lady Anne Blunt who saw him and did not approve of his stock, describes him as 'a useful horse but of no Arab type', but it should be remembered that Lady Anne's standards were exceptionally high.

He is entered in the French Stud Book, Volume 16, as being by a Kohel Cheyti

Amaveda (Count Rapello—Samaveda) bred by Mr. and Mrs. T. W. I. Hedley

horse out of a Managhieh Ibn Sbeyli mare. No mention is made of where he was bred.

In the General Stud Book he is entered thus:

El Emir (Sanad) a bay horse foaled about 1873, and imported by Miss Dillon in July 1880: his sire was a grey Kohel Cheyti horse, his dam a bay Managhieh Ibn Sbeyali. He was bred by Dehemedi Alzaba Ibn Amoud, and believed to have been exported to Algiers in November 1877, and was sold to the horse dealer, Mr. Charles Masne, and eventually became the property of Don Carlos Y Wactgin Y Arango, who sold him to Mr. John Legard, from whom Miss Dillon purchased him. He was a very well known horse in Algiers.

Again no mention is made of the country of his origin.

He appears to have been a versatile horse, of sweet temperament. Lady Anne records that his owner, Miss Dillon, used him for riding, driving and hunting, and that he was her favourite horse and accompanied her on all her travels.

Today, there is hardly a Stud that does not own a horse with El Emir blood.

Whatever his antecedents he has earned renown by appearing in the pedigrees of horses such as Nuri Pasha, Shahzada, Shihab, Manasseh, Aluf, Razada, Sala, Rizada, Rafeena, and the great Dargee through the female line of Ruth Kesia.

Maidan, is entered in the General Stud Book:

A chestnut horse, foaled in 1869, and bought of Abd er Rahman, of Bombay, by Col. Brownlow in 1871 (who received a certificate that he was pure bred). He was then sold to Major Brough, who sold him to Captain Fisher. He won the Kadir Cup (the blue ribbon of Pigsticking in India) and was then purchased by Lord Airlie. He spent three years in Afghanistan, and was imported into England by the Hon. Eustace Vesey, at whose death he was purchased of Mrs. Vesey by Miss Dillon, (15 hands).

Maidan is reported to have been a horse of great beauty and quality. He was absolutely sound at twenty-three, when he had to be destroyed because of a broken leg. As he appears in the pedigrees of several Crabbet bred horses it is obvious that his purity and excellence were accepted. One of his sons was Jamrood out of Jerud. Jamrood sired Haïl out of Hagar. Maidan's blood is also to be found

Astur (Indian Magic— Rissalma); bred by Mrs. E. M. Thomas

Azara (Manto—Incoronetta); bred by Mrs. E. M. Thomas

in America. It is recorded that he began racing at two years old. For three years from 1871 to 1874 Maidan raced and won, till no further matches could be made for him. Colonel Brownlow, a heavyweight of nineteen stone it is said, used him as his charger during the Afghanistan expedition. At 17 years of age, and after the death of Colonel Brownlow, Maidan was bought and raced again by Lord Airlie. He was then sold to the Honourable Eustace Vesey who shipped him to England on the troopship *Jumna*. They got as far as Suez where the ship met the expedition going to the relief of Saukin and was pressed into service as a troop ship. Maidan reached his destination, Marseilles, after 100 days of travel, during which he had not lain down once.

Mootrub, is described in the General Stud Book:

A Seglawi Jedrani, purchased in 1899 from Mr. Stewart Foster, who got him from Mr. Henderson, who bought him from General Sir John Hills, who bought him in India soon after Mootrub arrived from Arabia.

Mootrub's contribution to history is through the fame of his son Shahzada whose blood is found in most pedigrees in Australia.

Dwarka, the last imported Arabian to be entered in the General Stud Book was:

A bay horse (foaled about 1892) chosen especially by a friendly Arab Sheykh in the heart of the Anazeh country for General Ralph Broome, who took him to India in 1897 where he won many races. He was brought to England in 1901, and died in 1921.

There is no mention of his strain.

Dwarka introduced perhaps the most successful outcross to the Abbas-Pasha–Blunt bloodlines. He was acquired by H.R.H. the Prince of Wales (later, the Duke of Windsor), who bred Aldebaran out of the Abeyiah Sherrakieh mare Amida (Ibn Yashmak—Ajramieh of pure Blunt breeding.

Aldebaran sired by Rangha, a Crabbet bred mare, the beautiful Myra, a fine colt, Barkis, and Algol.

When the Duke of Windsor's Stud was dispersed, Algol was auctioned, and bought by Mr. George Ruxton, a breeder of great experience and knowledge. Algol has proved to be one of the most valuable outcrosses in Britain today. His

Cydella (General Grant —Domatella); bred by Mr. and Mrs. T. W. I. Hedley

Darjeel (Dargee—Rajjela); bred by Col. Sir Henry and Lady May Abel-Smith

blood is valued for the quality and beauty it imparts. His descendants Algoletta, Namilla, Mikeno and Dargee are names to be found today in the pedigrees of some of our best Arabians.

Of Skowronek, his importation, background and pedigree there can be no better account than that given by Count Joseph Potocki:

SKOWRONEK'S PEDIGREE AND THE ANTONINY STUD

Prince Roman Sanguszko (the elder) had an only daughter who was later to marry my grandfather, Alfred Potocki. It was in this way that a large part of the Sanguszko Stud, and land lying on the borders of Poland and the Ukraine came into my family by will in 1881 on the death of Prince Roman Sanguszko. It was destined to remain with us during the lifetime of only one generation since the treaty of Riga 1920 left nine-tenths of the property in Soviet territory and only one-tenth in the reconstituted free state of Poland.

Our country home on this property was called Antoniny. Prince Roman Sanguszko was born there in 1800. It was a broadly built country house with many dependencies. It had expanded as time went on within a lovely old park planted by an English landscape artist about 1800. Opposite the house were extensive stables which symbolized our close and constant connection with horses and breeding. In fact, the stables and riding school, used in more severe winter weather, were to us as it were a part of our home and it was hardly imaginable to stroll out in the morning without paying a visit to the horses and having a chat with the grooms.

Beyond the park, about half a mile away, there was another group of long stable buildings. That was the central stud establishment with its smaller and larger paddocks. Another great oak park of about a thousand acres stretched beyond them towards larger areas of farming land. The forests lay for about forty miles northward, mostly oak and beautiful pine. The country was by no means flat and the soil was rich and fertile.

To return to the Stud and its traditions, they certainly dated far back. Documents of the year 1528 show that three members of the Sanguszko family were giving 126 horses 'from their own Studs' for defence of the state. These Studs, according to the best sources, were always based on importations from the East. The later period since 1790 has been described more in detail. In 1803 a man named Burski went to the East (Arabia) and purchased several purebred

El Meluk (Mikeno—Mifaria); bred by The Lady Anne Lytton

Haroun (Hamif — Indian Snowflake); bred by Mr. M. A. Pitt-Rivers

Arabs for Prince Jerome Sanguszko to improve the existing Arab stock. In 1812 it was found necessary to hide the stud in the great forests for fear of confiscation or dispersal during the campaign which followed Napoleon's march on Russia. The son of the above mentioned Sanguszko, Prince Eustace Sanguszko, was taking part in that war as *aide-de-camp* of Prince Poniatowski on the side of Napoleon. This Eustace Sanguszko was a great lover of Arabs and also a good horseman. He had purchased in 1810 an Arab called Szumka I, well known for his great beauty. He organised expeditions to the East (Arabia) and succeeded in obtaining for his stud from the desert a number of purebred Arabs, Hajlan, Dzulfa and others.

At the time of this Sanguszko's death in 1844, his elder son, Prince Roman Sanguszko of Joseph Conrad's story and my great-grandfather, was in the Holy Land where he had gone on a pilgrimage directly after his liberation from Russian Siberia. He took this opportunity of purchasing in Arabia two stallions, Bat-Ran-Aga of the Seglawi and another called Djedran, as well as one mare, Elzana. Between 1850 and 1870, more good horses were bought for the Stud directly from the desert. Of the stallions bought by my father after he came into possession of the Stud, one of the best was Obejan, also named Euclid, purchased in India in 1890 from Lord William Beresford.

My father, of course, knew the Wilfrid Blunts and their Studs and had bought from them the great stallion Pharaoh (Faraon) whose four sons were sold from Antoniny in the 1890's to the Sultan of Turkey. Pharaoh had been imported from Arabia, in 1878 by the Blunts. Pharaoh, painted brilliantly by Lady Anne Blunt, with her husband Wilfrid up, is pictured as the frontispiece in Lady Wentworth's book, *The Authentic Arabian*.

Although Anglo-Arabs were also being bred for more general use at Antoniny, it remained a standing rule that the best Arab mares would invariably be covered by the leading pure bred Arab stallions.

As to Skowronek's sire, Ibrahim, he was purchased in 1907. Count Potocki continues:

My father, Count Joseph Potocki, Senior, who was at that time searching for a high class Arab stallion, received through his agents information that several

Greatheart (Irex—Garance) ; bred by the author

Indian Magic (Raktha —Indian Crown); bred by the late Lady Wentworth

Arabian horses had actually been obtained from the desert and were on their way via Constantinople, across the Black Sea to Odessa. He immediately sent an expert representative there and within a few days Ibrahim was purchased with a few other stallions of lesser quality. In looks, Ibrahim was perhaps even more striking than Skowronek and also proved to be a great sire. His head was slightly smaller than that of Skowronek, his coat, mane and exceptionally long white tail were silky to an extent which I do not remember in any other horse. On the other hand, Skowronek had perhaps a little more bone and better hocks, owing these good points, no doubt, to his dam, Jaskolka, one of our best mares.

Now there is one point which might seem puzzling with reference to Ibrahim. Why was it that his sire, Heijer, and dam, Lafitte, whose names were known and were inscribed in Skowronek's pedigree issued by me for the Arab Annex of Weatherby's General Stud Book, England, in September 1919 and July 1920, while the official Polish Stud Books published at a later date do not contain those names? The fact that the sire or dam (or both) of a horse coming from the Arabian desert are known is not so unusual. Such horses, however, were always registered in our stud books as 'Original Arab', 'Or. Ar.'. This means in our

Polish Stud Books 'Arabian horse originally from the Arabian desert'. No further additions were given except the strain from which they came if that was certain. In the case of Ibrahim, my father possessed the names of his sire and dam, Heijer and Lafitte, but inscribed him in our Stud Books in the above customary way. On the other hand, when the English owners of Skowronek expressed the wish to have these names included in his pedigree, my father did not raise any objection. When, however, some years later the Polish Arab Horse Society published the official Polish Stud Books of Arab Horses, it was considered preferable to keep strictly to the wording of the Antoniny Stud Books in which Ibrahim was defined as 'Original Arab' without any additions. The Polish Arab Horse Society preferred to quote the exact wording of our Stud Books to which it had full and free access and this was all the more comprehensive since all additional papers pertaining to Ibrahim had been lost in the business archives of Antoniny and could no longer be referred to.

The only authentic pedigree for Ibrahim's son is the one issued in Antoniny in accordance with our Stud Books and which, acting for my father, I confirmed in London in 1919 and 1920. Any extension on Ibrahim beyond his sire, Heijer, and dam, Lafitte, is not authentic. Ibrahim was the essence of breed and nobility.

In the late autumn of 1913, I had a glimpse of Skowronek in England when

Manto (Blue Domino—Mifaria); bred by the Lady Anne Lytton

Mikeno (Rissalix—Na-milla); bred by the late Miss G. M. Yule

visiting Mr. Winans, an American who had purchased him from my father in 1913. This was during my first term at Balliol College, Oxford. In 1914, the First World War severed for some years many of our personal contacts with the West of Europe.

The end of the lovely Ibrahim, sire of Skowronek, was truly dramatic. Some communist soldiers led him out of his box stall during the Revolution as other horses were being taken. Whereupon, that generally quiet and kindly horse began to react violently and would not be taken away. The troopers, in their irritation, killed him on the spot with their swords. The incident is described in a well known book *Pozoga*, by Zofia Kossak Szcyucka, who was there at the time.

I have jotted down these memories of Skowronek and Antoniny, hoping they may interest those who possess his offspring in their breeding establishments. I was also anxious to remove any doubts which may have arisen concerning his true and authentic pedigree. I would like to end this article with the warmest of tributes to that great horse, as well as to those who carry on the grand tradition of Arab breeding on many continents and more especially in the

United States. It is thanks to Skowronek more than to any other circumstance that Antoniny and its horse breeding establishment is still remembered even in distant lands. His name has become a precious link between Poland and lovers of the Arab horse in the United States of America.

The Antoniny Stud Books were saved after World War I, and Count Potocki retained them in Warsaw until 1939:

Some episodes in the early spring of 1918 gave us in the midst of destruction and material losses much reason for true and sincere satisfaction. The country all around Antoniny was by that time in a state of upheaval because of the Revolution, but the local population was not in the least hostile to us but continued to be friendly and make every effort to save and preserve. We owed to this attitude the saving of many objects from our country house and the possibility of taking them by various means to Warsaw. It was the local peasants who took some 56 cases of our books from Antoniny to a distant railroad station where they could be sent to Warsaw.

Thus, our library was saved and with it two thick volumes in folio, the Stud Books containing all the pedigrees of our horses, as well as the history of the

Fari II; bred by Mrs. R. H. Brown

Orion (Oran—Dancing Diamond); bred by the Crabbet Arabian Stud

Stud written by Prince Roman Sanguszko about 1870. Later I completed his story with a detailed account of events in the Stud during the first World War and its aftermath, the Russian Revolution. I wrote it myself and enumerated all the Stud's horses which were saved during that period.

Before leaving my house in Warsaw, I put the Stud Books in what I considered a safe place. In 1944 the house was completely gutted by fire during the Warsaw Insurrection. Unless taken in previous looting, they are presumed destroyed by fire.*

* The above notes on the pedigree of Skow-ronek and the Antoniny Stud Books are quoted by courtesy of Mrs. Milton Thompson to whom they were given by Count Joseph Potocki.

Up to the year 1957 the breeding of Arabians in Britain followed a conservative pattern, which had proved so successful that their bloodlines were sought in every country where Arabians are bred. They were particularly desired as foundation stock. The leading Studs in England would admit no bloodlines other than those registered in the General Stud Book, in other words, the concentrated Abbas Pasha-Blunt blood, with the exception of the four horses mentioned earlier in this chapter.

The foreseeable result of the reduction in size of the Crabbet Stud and the dispersal of almost all the Hanstead horses was an increase in the number of smaller

Studs. The majority having been founded on mares registered in the General Stud Book it might have been possible to distribute the legacy of valuable stock that remained had it not been for the shortage of stallions. Through the generosity of Miss Gladys Yule, the services of Hanstead's finest stallions had been made available to outside mares. Stallions like Rissalix, Grey Owl, General Grant, Count Dorsaz and Blue Domino had sired some of the best stock in the country, but now Stud owners had to depend on buying or breeding a stallion for their own mares, always a perplexing situation for a small Stud.

After the death of Lady Wentworth, the new owner of Crabbet, Mr. Cecil Covey, kindly offered the services of the Crabbet stallions to outside mares. The stallions Oran, Bright Shadow, Indian Magic and for a time, Silver Vanity, Grand Royal and Dargee were still available and have helped to replenish the existing stock.

The last named stallion, Dargee, was bred by Mr. George Ruxton, one of the founder members of the Arab Horse Society, and bought as a yearling by Lady Wentworth. Though he was of Abbas-Pasha–Blunt blood only on his dam's side he has sired stock of the most refined, classic type, and many breeders have had reason to be grateful for this acquisition to Crabbet.

Rajmek (Mikeno—Rajjela); bred by Col. Sir Henry and Lady May Abel-Smith

Radfan (Dancing King —Bint Yasimet); bred by Mr. and Mrs. D. D. Wright

Yet this did not solve the problem of the next generation of stallions. The two great Studs were able to select and retain only the best of a large number of colts. More important still, the sires so selected could be mated with a variety of the finest mares. For smaller Studs this ideal procedure is not possible and the potential excellence of some of the younger stallions may never be discovered.

Again, depending on the maintenance of stallions at Hanstead and Crabbet many of the best young colts bred by other Studs were sold abroad.

Though many dominant sires remained in England after 1957 the export of so many of the best mares from the major Studs in that year resulted in an ever-lessening supply of young stallions bred on the lines that had proved so successful. The only alternative was to import, but from what source? To those brought up in the Abbas-Pasha–Blunt tradition it seemed unthinkable that any outside blood could be lightly considered. Miss Patricia Lindsay of Stockings Farm took the initiative by visiting Poland in 1958, and was much impressed by the Arabians being bred there. As a result of her visit she imported:

The stallions: Gerwazy (Doktryner—Gwara) bred at the Michalow Stud,

Grójec (Comet—Gastronomia). The mares: Czantoria (Wielki Szlem—Mordzana), Celina (Witraz—Elza), Carmencita (El Haifi—Carmen), Damietta (Trypolis—Dimatra), Gehenna (Doktryner—Gazella), Karramba (Witraz—Carmen).

Subsequently, Celina was bought by Mr. H. V. Musgrave Clark of the Courthouse Stud. Carmencita, by Miss Lyon's Harwood Stud. Gehenna, by Mrs. Murray of the Painswick Stud, and Damietta went overseas to Mr. Frank Smathers in Florida. The stallion Grojec joined the Blunt Stud owned by Lady Anne Lytton.

There was a parallel in many of the blood-lines of these horses to the early Blunt imports. In conformation, size and proportions of the head they more nearly resembled the desert-Arabian than the English-bred horses. They had markedly good legs and shoulders.

So favourable was the impression they created, and remembering the remarkable impact of Skowronek, other Polish imports followed:

The mares Latawica (Wielki Szlem—Larissa), Lafirynda (Miecznik—Lala); Almaviva (Wielki Szlem—Alhambra); Arwila (Amurath Sahib—Wilga) and Camera (Aquinor—Canberra), joined the band at Stockings Farm.

The mares Nawarra (Trypolis—Najada) and Barcelona (Doktryner—Brussa) were imported by the Marchioness Townshead and Mrs. A. J. Sellars respectively. The mare Biruta (Trypolis—Bika) by Lord Moyne's Biddesden Stud; Mufta (Mlech Pelinski—Atfa), by the Briery Close Stud, and the stallion Argos, a beautiful son of Nabor ex Arfa, by Mr. J. Alexander.

Argos has earned Supreme awards at the Arab Horse Society's Show at Kempton Park as Senior Stallion; as well as Ridden Stallion. He has sired prize-winners of good type. Grojec has won Honours in the Show ring, and is a popular sire. Gerwazy is a perfectly-mannered 'storybook Arabian' under saddle and has his share of Championships.

Of the mares, Celina and Karramba have both won Championships at the Society's Show.

The next imports were from Russia. In the early 1960's, consignments of horses bred at the Ministry of Agriculture's State Farms in the U.S.S.R. came to Crippenden Manor, Sussex, to be trained and sold as riding horses. There were Akhal-Teke, Tersky, Budenov, Anglo-Arabs, Thoroughbreds, and a few Arabians.

Crippenden Manor was perfectly designed for this purpose and managed on the most modern lines. These horses were all of fine riding-type and found ready buyers. Arabian breeders were glad of this opportunity to see the type of pure-bred being produced in Russia and several were selected by individual Studs.

Miss Margaret Evans of Edge Hill Stud bought two stallions; Naply (Pomeranets—Nitochka) and Listopad (Pomeranets—Laba). The mare Kaplja was

Roxan (Count Roland—Bint Roxana); bred by Miss M. J. Stevens

Shammar (Champurrado—Somra II); bred by H. V. Musgrave Clark

bought by Mrs. E. M. Thomas of the Metcombe Stud in Devon. She was sired by Pomeranets, by Priboj (Piolun—Rissalma) ex Mamoona (Ofir-Krucica). Her dam was Klinika, by Korej (Kann—Rixalina) out of Naturalistka (Naseem—Rissalma). Kaplja's pedigree is given in some detail because it is of interest that it contains some of the best of both English and Polish blood.*

Sunlights Allegro (Indian King—Dancing Sunlight); bred by R. M. Kydd

A stallion, Capriznaya of identical breeding also came to England at this time, as also the mare Manipuljazia (Pomeranets—Madila) now owned by the Kloof Arabian Stud, and the stallion Nameshnik (Arax—Neposeda) owned by the Horsey Island Stud.

The pedigrees of the Russian-bred stallions and mares were accepted in the English Stud-books only if they traced in all lines to Crabbet or Polish origins.

In 1965 Miss Margaret Evans visited Russia and brought back four mares from the State Stud. One of these mares, the grey Naprasalina, has classic type and beauty at its best. She was then 18 years old, and in foal to Aswan, an Egyptian-bred stallion by Nazeer out of Tuzra by Sheik al Arab, largely descended from Blunt stock.

Naprasalina is the daughter of Nomer (ex Pletka), a grandson of Naseem. She won the Supreme Championship at Kempton Park in 1967; her filly Nadirah, by Aswan, won Firsts as a foal and as a yearling.

The other mares were Panorama (Negativ—Privilegia); Speshka (Priboj—Sofa

* Another mare in this category, now owned by the Rodanieh Stud, is Nahodka, by Knippel (Korej—Florencia) out of Novizna (Naseem—Nizgoda).

II) and Maritsa (Arax—Monopolia).

In 1968, the Briery Close Stud, owned by Major and Mrs. T. W. I. Hedley, one of the largest Studs in England, imported from America a young stallion of pure Egyptian blood, The Shah (Fabah—Bint Fada); his pedigree goes back to the first imports made by Henry Babson from the Egyptian Royal Agricultural Society in 1932.

The introduction of fresh blood-lines, similar though they may be to those established by the Blunts, is an experiment of some significance.

Each newcomer brings with it a reputation based on its history. Reputation and observation are not the same; and here lies the problem. In England, the observation of the stock which are the foundation of the finest blood-lines in the world, their succeeding generations, and their co-lateral descendants have been the education of breeders in the country.

Reputation is the sum-total of a variety of opinions.

The achievements of both Polish and Russian horses is recorded in their respective Stud Books almost entirely on speed and performance on the race-track. Their ability to transmit speed and stamina to their progeny is their highest recommendation; while in England breeders have adhered to the theories upheld and exemplified by the Blunts, that type and quality, and the ability to perpetuate

Silver Sheen (Bright Shadow—Silver Grey); bred by the Crabbet Stud

these in their progeny is the only yardstick by which the value of Arabians can be measured.

It has yet to be proved whether the blood-lines imported since 1957 will result in the emergence of any outstanding stallion or mare to compare with the great ones of the past.

In Britain there has been a remarkable resurgence of interest in the Arabian. Those who were fortunate enough to own Hanstead and Crabbet-bred mares have bred from them, using the dominant sires still surviving or sons of dominant sires.

Of the *Dominant Sires* available in 1957 these are still serving:

Bright Shadow (Radi—Pale Shadow)
General Grant (Raktha—Samsie)
Indian Magic (Raktha—Indian Crown)

Sons of Dominant Sires available in 1969:

Of Rissalix: Mikeno, ex Namilla
             Rimini, ex Mirvanah
Of Oran: Ayton Rebel ex Nuhraa
         Forano, ex Farette
         Indian King, ex Indian Pride
         Brandreth, ex Gleaming Gold
         Orion, ex Dancing Diamond
Of Raktha: General Grant
           Indian Magic
           Rissani ex Rosalina
Of Irex: Alexus ex Aletta
        Champurrado ex Niseyra
        Greatheart ex Garance
        Iridos ex Rafeena
Of Silver Vanity: Hanif ex Sirella
                Rayyan ex Rissefa
Of Grand Royal: Ayton Royal ex Zehraa
Of Dargee: Darjeel ex Rajjela

           Magnet ex Rosalina
Of Grey Owl: Nimran ex Nurmahal
Of Rangoon: None
Of Blue Domino: Blue Grotto ex Shamnar
             Blue Halo ex Aleya
             Fari ex Farette

Silver Grey (Royal Diamond—Silver Gilt); bred by the late Lady Wentworth

Fari II
Hascmet ex Eloia
Jamshid of Knotting ex Riffila
Kerim ex Hedba
Ludo ex Rithyana
Manto ex Mifaria
Rahlind ex Colinda
Of Count Dorsaz: Count Ambrino ex Ambria
Count Orlando ex Umatella
Oredan ex Rediaa
Count Rapello ex Rithyana
Count Roland ex Rithyana
Razmak ex Mohra

The early situation has been reversed; there are now very many fine mares in the country and a shortage of younger stallions worthy of them.

In 1969, fifty-one years after the foundation of the Arab Horse Society, there were more breeders and owners than ever in its history. The number of registered horses was approximately 2,500, a spectacular rise since the end of the war in 1945, when a liberal estimate would place the total at 400.

The Society's Show at Kempton Park in the summer of 1969 extended for three days, to include Classes for 700 entries of the finest Arabians, Anglo-Arabs, and Part-bred Arabians in the country, and of an excellence which could not be bettered anywhere in the world.

Chapter 8

Australia

FEW COUNTRIES in the world are as ideally suited to the breeding of the Arabian horse as Australia, where the space and climatic environment closely resemble that of his homeland. It is a land where the riding horse is an integral part of life.

Arabian horses from the Crabbet Stud were imported as long ago as 1891, when Sir James Penn Boucaut founded the Quambi Stud in South Australia. He purchased the stallion Rafyk (Azrek—Rose of Sharon), and the mares Rose of Jericho (Kars—Rodania); and Dahna (Kars—Dahma). Ten years later he imported Faraoun (Mesaoud—Faulana) and the mare Namusa (Ahmar—Narghileh) also Crabbet-bred. Bedaween, champion Stallion of Australia was bred at this Stud. He was by Rafyk ex Rose of Jericho.

When Sir James Penn Boucaut died in 1908 his Stud was dispersed. Fortunately some of the surviving imports and their stock were acquired by two breeders who knew their value. The Honourable Samuel Winter-Cooke of Murandal, Victoria purchased the largest number and this preserved from dispersal this fine nucleus of Crabbet-bred Arabians. Mr. G. Leonard Brown purchased at the Quambi Sale three mares of pure Crabbet blood, Seykh, Rabi and Ayesha, full sisters, by Rafyk—Namusa. He later imported the stallion Harir (Berk—Hamasa) from Crabbet.

Another contemporary importation that is a major influence in the breeding of Arabians in Australia today was that made by A. E. Grace of Bowral, New South Wales. In 1922 he bought from Mr. C. Hough of Hydes, Abridge, Essex, the stallion Shahzada, winner of two Endurance Tests in England. He was by the desert-bred horse Mootrub, out of Ruth Kesia who traces back to El Emir.

In succeeding years Mr. Grace imported the stallions Sheelook, a son of Shahzada out of Hubara; Nazar, by Nuri Sherif out of Nezza, a daughter of Shahzada; the mares Shahin (Sheelook—Hubara); the Crabbet-bred mare Miriam (Nadir—Ranya) and the desert-bred mare Nejdmieh.

After the First World War, during which the demand for light horses for military use had been urgent, interest in the breeding and quality of such horses grew remarkably. Appreciation of the Arabian, both as a pure-bred, and as an improver of the native stock chiefly derived from the Thoroughbred, became increasingly evident.

In 1928, Winter-Cooke died and his Stud was for sale. Many of the horses were sold and their subsequent records lost but there were now several established

Nefertiti (Count Manilla—Tou-fail); bred and owned by Mrs. E. Bligh

Brinsissa (Abiram—Kastana); bred and owned by Mrs. E. Bligh

Miraya (Crystal Fire—Fantasy); bred and owned by Mrs. E. Bligh

Sirocco (Crystal Fire—Scherzade); bred and owned by Mrs. E. Bligh

Chiffon (Sindh—Carlina); bred and owned by Mrs. A. D. Maclean

Brigadier (Sindh—Brilliant); bred and owned by Mrs. A. D. Maclean

breeders who were interested in acquiring his stock to augment their own.

Mrs. Dora MacLean of Yan Yean, Victoria, purchased three mares. Asil (Rafyk—Al Caswa), Johara (Fakreddin—Asil), and Zem-Zem (Fakreddin—Saade).

Mr. A. J. McDonald, of Dubbo, New South Wales, bought from the Quambi Sale, the stallions Rafyk (Azrek—Rose of Sharon), Raisuli (Rief—Ayesha) and Faraoun. These stallions were used to establish bloodlines which are the foundations of many Arabian Studs today.

Faraoun was later sold to Russia.

Another breeder interested in the dispersal of the Winter-Cooke horses was Mr. J. F. Jelbart of Stony Park East, Jindera, New South Wales. He founded his Stud in 1930 on three mares bought at the Quambi Sale. They were Kufara, Mena, and Mecca II, daughter of the mare Al Caswa (Rafyk—El Zahr), who was a grand-daughter of El Emir. They were sired by the Crabbet stallions Fakreddin and Khamasin. From A. E. Grace he bought Judith (Shahzada—Miriam) and from Leonard Brown, two mares of pure Crabbet blood, Salaam and Sa-id, both by Harir out of Sekh.

After twenty years of success Mr. Jelbart decided to retire, but rather than disperse what had grown to be one of the leading Studs in Australia, he approached the New South Wales Department of Agriculture. They wisely accepted his offer

Nickel (Silver Moon-light—Moonoura); bred and owned by Mrs. A. D. Maclean

and incorporated part of his stock including eighteen of his best mares with theirs to form the basis of a State Stud at Hawkesbury and Wagga Agricultural College. At the time their resident stallion was Ghenghiz Khan (Shahzada—Miriam) bred by A. E. Grace.

Today, though very well provided with stock of their own breeding, the College, founded in 1949, imports from time to time, stallions from England to reinforce their bloodlines.

Sala (Grey Owl—Hama) bred at Hanstead came in 1947. On his dam's side he has the same bloodlines as Shahzada.

Razaz (Champurrado—Rahab) winner of Championships in England as well as in Australia, was imported in 1955. He is of pure Crabbet blood, and bred by Mr. H. V. Musgrave Clark. His stock are noted for their refinement and good, compact conformation.

Very recently the College considered the infusion of Polish blood and purchased a bay horse, Cyrasa (Comet—Barcelona), bred by Mrs. Sellars of Treeyews Stud in England. It should be interesting to see the influence of his breeding in Australia.

The greatest concentration of Crabbet blood, and the Stud that has done most to help new breeders to establish themselves, is at the Fenwick Stud Farm, at Yan Yean near Melbourne, owned by Mrs. Dora MacLean.

This Stud was founded in 1925 with the purchase from Crabbet of the mare Rafina (Rustem—Risala), with the colt foal Raseel (by Nureddin) at foot. The three mares bought at the Quambi Sale and the Crabbet-bred stallion Harir augmented her stock. Since then a number of stallions and mares from Crabbet and Hanstead have added to the distinguished record of the Fenwick Stud.

In succession came the stallions Rakib (Nax—Rythama); Indian Light (Naseem—Nisreen); Silver Sparkle (Oran—Silver Fire); Electric Silver (Raktha —Silfina) and Silver Moonlight (Indian Magic—Silver Fire).

From Crabbet also came the fine mares Nazirieh (Skowronek—Nisreen); Nuralina (Hazzam—Nasira) and Rizla (Rissam—Ghezala). In 1947, Carlina (Rissam—Shamnar) was bought from Hanstead, and the famous Riffal (Naufal— Razina). Riffal, standing 16 hands high, though of unusual height for an Arabian, had a classic head and neck and splendid conformation; qualities which are evident in his stock. His finest legacy to England was his great son Oran.

Shafreyn (Royal Diamond—Sharfina), a big prize-winner in Australia, was imported about 1952, and most recently Mrs. MacLean imported Sindh, a very handsome son of Silver Vanity, one of the finest stallions ever bred at Crabbet. Sindh has proved an outstanding stallion whose stock is eagerly sought after for its uniform excellence. The value of the blood lines of these horses to the Arabian in Australia today can hardly be over-estimated.

A smaller Stud that has selected its foundation stock with the utmost care is at

Bostocks, Queensland, owned by Mrs. E. K. Bligh and her daughter Elizabeth. Horses bred here are of outstanding Arabian type. One of their most successful stallions, who succeeded the older Nekhl (Rashid II—Nasirieh), and Crystal Magic (Dargee—Rosinella) being Count Manilla (Count Dorsaz—Namilla) bred at the Hanstead Stud. Two mares of Crabbet and Hanstead bloodlines who, besides being prize winners themselves, have produced superior stock, are

Aethon   (Spindrift— Hestia) ; bred and owned by Mrs. C. Proudford

Scherzade (Irex—Shamal) and Dominita (Blue Domino—Teresita) both bred at the Well House Stud, Sussex. The latest importation to come to Bostocks was the bay stallion Abiram (Noran—Rythoura) bred in Holland at Dr. Houtappels' Rodania Stud.

The Queensland Agricultural College, at Lawes under the direction of Mr. F. R. Staunton, is the second State-owned Stud. Much of its foundation stock was acquired from the Pennant Hills Stud of Mr. and Mrs. Leicht who had imported the Crabbet-bred horses Rosarial (Fayal—Naxina), Silwan (Dargee—Silwa), Spindrift (Silver Drift—Silver Grand) and Silver Magic (Indian Magic—Silver Fire) between the years 1948–1958.

In 1959, the College imported Grand Royal (Oran—Sharima) from Crabbet Park. He is a horse of magnificent presence, and many times champion in England. Silver Moonlight was here also before he was sold to America.

The State-owned Stud Farms compete with private breeders in open classes at the Shows. The capital city in each State has its own Agricultural Show (the Melbourne and Sydney Shows are designated Royal) held annually, with several classes for Arabians in hand, and two or three Championship classes. The Royal Melbourne includes two ridden classes.

A more recent establishment that is breeding excellent stock is the Santarabia Stud owned by Mr. Leo Campbell of Luddenham, New South Wales. He has selected mares of proven bloodlines and his senior stallion is by Sindh; another is by Riffal. An aged stallion of superlative breeding who was imported in utero in 1951 is by Irex—Quaker Girl, and there are two imported half-Polish colts who were bred in England. One by Blue Halo—Barcelona, and the other by a Nabor son, Argos out of the Count Dorsaz daughter Perle D'Or.

The bloodlines selected by Mr. Campbell could hardly be bettered; this is a Stud that has much to contribute to Arabian breeding in Australia.

Three other senior breeders whose work should be recorded are: Dr. Crozier of Barnoolut, Victoria, Mrs. C. Lucock of Ennerdale, Dundonnell, Victoria, and Dr. C. H. Leggett, owner of the Oxford Stud, Brisbane, Queensland.

It is not possible here to list the many other Stud Farms being developed in Australia today, some as business organisations and others by dedicated individuals.

Because of the vast distances overland, and the great expense and risk of importing horses to this Continent, Arabian breeders have, in the past, been obliged to do the best with such stock as was already in the country. This resulted in intensive in-breeding to Shahzada bloodlines. His dam tracing back two generations to the Blunt importation, Azrek, also traces three generations back on her dam's side to El Emir, imported by Miss Dillon. There are comparatively few Arabians in Australia today who do not trace to this lineage.

Another disadvantage was, that a stallion, once imported, had to be used whether he produced first-class stock or not; he was too expensive to discard.

Today, taking advantage of modern speed and ease of transport, breeders are able not only to import stock from abroad but to select them personally and, in the case of stallions, to evaluate their breeding potential.

With the economic growth and development of the continent, and the accompanying increase in population and the prosperity of its people, there has been a remarkable revival of interest in the Arabian.

The ownership and breeding of Arabians has become the portrait of prosperity.

The Arabian's most successful rival is the Quarter Horse, a comparative newcomer to Australia. Trained and bred by American land-owners who have come to live in the country, they are popular for their 'handiness', and eminently suitable for 'station-work'.

Polo, Polo-Cross and Show-jumping, have long been popular, and the

Babylon (Razaz—Alaga Girl); bred by the Department of Agriculture

Carthage (Razaz—Pallas); bred by the Department of Agriculture

Thoroughbred has always been regarded as the obvious choice for these activities. Today, the Part-breds and Anglo-Arabs are coming to the fore, and to a lesser extent the pure-bred. But in Cross-country riding and Endurance Tests, the Arabian has proved himself superior to all other breeds.

The governing body of the Arab Horse Society of Australasia has instituted State Divisions to promote and guard the interests of the horse, within the State.

Today, there exist State Divisions in Queensland, New South Wales, Victoria, and Australian Capital Territory (Southern Division). Western Australia and South Australia are in the process of establishing Divisions.

Within these Divisions there is latitude in the methods adopted to encourage the use of Arabians. The Queensland Division recently conducted a Performance School with Instructors from the U.S.A. to demonstrate how to train Arabians for the Show-ring, and for the new and varied Classes in which they are now encouraged to compete.

There is a promising future for the Australian-bred Arabian, with this proviso. That breeders give the greatest consideration to the value of imported bloodlines, which are needed to obviate the effects of earlier in-breeding, giving priority to those individuals who in their pedigrees and in their progeny have consistently portrayed the best type. Type which should be of a classic and international standard, rather than that favoured by this or that country, or governed by the elusive factors of the Show Ring.

Chapter 9

Bahrain

THE AUTHOR is indebted for this account of the Arabian horses of Bahrain to a recent visitor, Mrs. V. Noli-Marais, who is herself a breeder of Arabians:

I was led to Bahrain by the writings of Lady Anne Blunt. I found that she had written in 1917, 'There are also in Arabia certain Studs still flourishing in the hands of Princes and individuals which are recognised as authentic.'*

The chief of these are the Studs of:

The Ibn Raschids of Hail

Aid el Tenim at Oneyza

Emir Ibn Khalifa of Bahreyn

Sultan of Muscat

King Ibn Saoud

The Alkhalifa family, which has ruled Bahrain without interruption since 1782, originally belonged to the Anazeh tribe of central Nejd, which possessed the best horses according to Major Upton.**

In 1716 the Bani Utbah clan of the Anazeh, consisting of the three families of the Khalifa – later of Bahrain; the Sabbah – later of Kuwait; and the Jalahma, gave up its nomad habits and, together with their horses, settled on the site of the present town of Kuwait.

In 1782 Ahmed Alkhalifa captured Bahrain from the Persians, and the Alkhalifa family has ruled there since. This has resulted in a continuity in the breeding of pure Arabian horses by the ruling family. Unlike the rest of Arabia, the island was prosperous long before the discovery of oil, because of its strategic position, fresh water springs, and ancient Pearling Industry.

The present Ruler, His Highness Sheik Isa bin Sulman Alkhalifa, is the tenth Sheik of the Khalifa family to inherit the Alkhalifa family Stud and to rule Bahrain and its dependencies. The Alkhalifas have preserved the horse-breeding heritage of the Anazeh and have continued their breeding according to the old Bedu traditions.

Abbas Pasha of Egypt, who ruled from 1848 to 1854, and was known to possess the finest horses in Arabia, also added to his collection three mares bought from the Khalifas of Bahrain. These were a Seglawieh Jedranieh, and two Dahmeh Shahwanieh.***

In 1863 Palgrave, who was not a horse-lover, in passing through Bahrain

* *Gleanings from the Desert of Arabia*, 1882, page 228.

** *Thoroughbred Racing Stock*, Lady Wentworth, page 80.

*** *The Authentic Arabian*, Lady Wentworth

referred to 'the handsome Stud of Mohammed Alkhalifa'.*

The State consists of a group of islands of a desert nature, about 230 square miles, and situated in the Arabian Gulf about 15 miles from the mainland of Arabia. Unlike the rest of Arabia, Bahrain has many Artesian wells around which gardens are laid out, with lucerne, fruit trees and date palms.

The Royal Stud approximates 300 of the choicest of the old family strains. The stallion is chosen from only six of the strains; namely, Jellabi, Krushan, Dahman, Shawaf, Wathnan, and Mlolshan. The Krush strain is one of the rarest in the world. Lady Anne Blunt records that it was the proud monopoly of the Muteyr tribe.

The stallion selected must be masculine-looking, with a wedge-shaped head, large eyes, wide forehead, long but powerful neck, broad chest, short back, long fore-arms, large feet and a thin skin.

The horses are mostly bright copper bays with black points, secondly flea-bitten greys, and lastly a few chestnuts. Some had flashy white markings, and two of the chestnuts had light manes and tails.

The horses are kept in groups in various parts of the island. Near the Ruler's

Krushan. One of the 5 Arabian stallions in the Royal Stud belonging to H. H. Sheik Isa Bin Sulman Alkhalifa, Ruler of Bahrain

Central and Eastern Arabia, 1862, Palgrave, page 225.

main palace at Rufaa, there are four stabling groups, each housing about forty horses. The stables are built in the form of a huge square, the doors facing into a quadrangle which has been surfaced with a layer of fine sand.

During the day, the horses stand shackled by one front pastern to cement blocks buried in the sand. Pregnant mares and those with foals at foot are allowed out to pasture during the day.

In the morning freshly-cut lucerne is fed. The main meal at 5 p.m. consists of a mash prepared in a large shallow cement trough. The mash consists of three sacks of broad bran, five sacks uncrushed barley, ten baskets of pressed unstoned dates, spread out in layers. This is damped with water and thoroughly mixed by hand. The mixture is allowed to stand for four hours before feeding. The horses are adept at spitting out the date-stones, although their teeth rather suffer in the process. When they have finished their meal, a layer of clean date stones line the bottom of each manger. The dates prove to be digestible even for the youngest foals. Stallions have a record life-span of usefulness, some being active sires at the age of twenty-eight and thirty years.

It was a most interesting experience to see here the type of Arabian pure in descent from those seen by the envoys of Abbas Pasha, and Lady Anne Blunt a century or more ago.

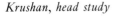

Krushan, head study

Almost a century later a link was forged in England with the Arabians from this distant Eastern land with whom they have a common heritage. The Arab Horse Society's Stud Book Vol. 6 contains this entry:

Nuhra (1936) Sire A Kehailan Al Jellabi
Dam A Kehailan Al Wadhnieh (Khursanieh)
Breeder H.H. The Sheikh of Bahrein
Presented to Major-General the Rt. Hon. the Earl of Athlone, K.G. by
H.H. The Sheikh of Bahrain in 1939.

Nuhra has made no small contribution to the country of her adoption. Among her progeny are Rabiha (by Rehoboam) dam of Sheba and Ayton Rasila both by Silver Vanity, and of Romana by Blue Domino, all prize winners; Rediaa (by Rehoboam), the dam of Oredan by Count Dorsaz. Oredan sired the Anglo-Arab Carbrook Surprise, winner of one of the most coveted prizes of the year, The Frederick Trophy at the Horse of the Year Show; Nurmana the dam of Zehraa, by Irex, she the dam of Alzehraa by Count Dorsaz, and of Ayton Royal by Oran; Nuhajjela (by Irex), the dam of Rajjela by Grand Royal; Rajjela is the dam of the two Supreme Champions Rajmek, by Mikeno; and Darjeel, by Dargee.

This distinguished band, descendants of the Bahraini mare, Nuhra, were bred at the Barton Lodge Stud, Windsor, home of Sir Henry and Lady May Abel Smith. Lady May is the daughter of H.R.H. Princess Alice, Countess of Athlone.

Chapter 10

Egypt

THE TYPE of Egyptian horse is known to us, from as early as the 18th dynasty, when horses were being portrayed on Egyptian monuments which would serve as models for the classic Arabian of today.

It is almost impossible to trace the history of the horse in Egypt at all continuously, but from the 13th century A.D. onwards more details are available. By this time Egypt had fallen far behind Arabia as a horse producing country, and to regain her position she had to import desert-bred strains, based on the very stock she had herself sent northwards 2,000 years previously, in her wars in Syria.

By the 18th century, Studs of such size and magnificence were being maintained by the Egyptian Viceroys and Pashas as have never been equalled. Their subsequent history is told in an earlier chapter; in their decline and the dispersal of their stock these Studs enriched the world.

In 1908, a State controlled body, the Egyptian Horse Breeding Commission was set up, later called the Royal Agricultural Society, and today with its wider implications, the Egyptian Agricultural Organization. It was the Egyptian Horse Breeding Commission, represented by Mr. Trouncer who purchased from the Blunts the horses left at Sheykh Obeyd when they decided to move their Stud to England.

Lady Anne at this time generously presented to the Egyptian Agricultural Stud, the stallion Jamil (Aziz Bint—Jamila), and the mares Jamila and Bint Yemama.

Jamil sired Mansour, sire of Roda and Nazeer. Bint Yemama was the dam of Negma, who has amongst her descendants such famous horses as Mahroussa, Aziza, Maaroufa, Fadl, Zarif, Hamida, Hamama and Nasr.

In 1920, the Egyptian Princes imported twenty horses from the Crabbet Stud, including Ibn Yashmak (Feysul—Yashmak), El Borak, Rustem and Razaz.

Some of the finest descendants of these horses and of the earlier acquisitions are to be found in the United States today.

In succeeding years, while the country lived through a period of political upheaval and readjustment, little was heard of Arabians being bred in Egypt except for racing. But there always existed a few private Studs owning horses of the purest blood and superlative foundation stock, such as that of Prince Mohamed Ali at Manial on the island of Roda; of Prince Kemal el Dine at Saft; and Mr. T. B. G. Trouncer of Sidi Salem.

An interesting account of the Royal Agricultural Society's Stud Farm at Kafr

Farouk in 1937, and the Sidi Salem Stud owned by Mr. Trouncer, was written
by the Director General of the Royal Agricultural Society, His Excellency Fouad
Abaza. His comments on the type and quality of the horses he saw at that time
are worth recording:

A visit to the Royal Agricultural Society's Stud Farm at Kafr Farouk
in 1937, by his Excellency Fouad Abaza.

To all those racing men and women whose foremost interest is the Arab horse,
I cannot too strongly recommend a visit to the Royal Agricultural Society's
Stud Farm at Kafr Farouk, and all those who go there will find their trouble
well repaid. My visit, which was paid in company with Dr. Mabrouk, proved
to be one of the most interesting I have made to any stables in Egypt up to the
present day, and my best thanks are due to Dr. Mabrouk and Dr. Ashoub for
the kindness they showed me before, during and after my visit. For much
information incorporated in this account I am grateful to these gentlemen and
hereby acknowledge my indebtedness to them.

To reach Kafr Farouk one has to take a car, and after passing the main road
from Heliopolis and Zeitoun, S. Michaelides' racing stables are passed, and
then approaching Ein Shams a sharp turn is made to the right, out into the
desert. The track after that leads directly to the Stud Farm, which is situated
in an ideal place for breeding purposes. The Stud Farm is a very big place, with
an acreage of fifty-five feddans. On the right as one enters is a small field of
bersim, which is the only green stuff in the district. Immediately at the bottom
of the fields are the stallions' stables and it is from then onwards that the visit
proper begins.

And now a few words regarding the Society's efforts at breeding and the
growth of their industry would not be out of place. In 1908 the Society was
using English thoroughbreds for stallions in order to improve the breed, which
had shown signs of some deterioration. The Society continued with this policy
until 1914, when it became only too apparent that the half-breds were ugly,
inclined to the vicious, and that people were taking a strong dislike to them.

As a result of discussions and private observations the Society decided to
replace the thoroughbreds by Arab pedigree stallions. That, however, was
easier said than done. The best pedigree Arab stallions at that time were few
and far between in Egypt, and only those that had been bred by Abbas Pasha I
were found to be good enough for the Society's purpose, and therefore, the
Society was forced to fall back on their last line; that is breeding. Thus it came
about that in 1914 a few mares and horses were obtained from the stables of
H.H. Abbas Pasha II at Kobbeh, from H.H. Prince Mohammed Ali whose
stables were at Map and Lady Anne Blunt, who had a breeding establishment

at Ein Shams. Later others were imported from the Crabbet Stud, the property of Lady Wentworth in Sussex, England.

These experiments proved highly successful, and it came about that in 1929 spacious stables with large paddocks, were erected at Kafr Farouk, near Ein Shams, on a sandy spot ideal in every respect for horse breeding.

At present the Society has at the Stud Farm thirty pure Arab mares and forty-two head of colts and fillies. In addition fifty pedigree Arab stallions are distributed in the various districts of Egypt for the purpose of serving native mares. It will thus be seen that the Society has made rapid progress towards the achievement of its ambition.

The dearest wish of the Society is that some day in the near future Egypt will take her place in the East, and thus oust and displace Arabia in producing the best and purest-bred Arab Stock, and become the most important centre of Arab horse breeding in the world.

In 1932 the Society sold three yearlings to Mr. Henry Babson, America, for £E.675, and in 1933 one colt was also sold to America at a cost of £E.300. In 1936 five fillies were sold to the Italian Government for £E.1,500. The Society is now leasing some of their colts for racing purposes, and other animals are being trained on the Stud Farm at Kafr Farouk for the race track.

The following stallions are posted in the Society's Studs. Guezireh, Fayed, Radi, Balance, Kazmeyn, Ibn Rustem and Gazlan. Bahtim, Ibn Manial, Ibn

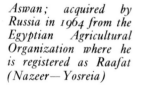

Aswan; acquired by Russia in 1964 from the Egyptian Agricultural Organization where he is registered as Raafat (Nazeer—Yosreia)

Dura, Rabeh and Ibn Radia. Kafr Farouk, Ibn Rabdan, Mansour and Ibn Samhan Dareh.

As I entered the farm I was able to see a colt of two and a half years being trained for the race track. He was being ridden bareback by a Bedouin, who held the reins in his mouth, his hands hanging loosely by his side, and occasionally stroking the colt. Trotting up and down the roadway the colt was made to pass the car, and although he trembled in every limb as the chauffeur revved up the engine, he was under perfect control and behaved himself like a gentleman. Dr. Ashoub then joined the party and after a brief visit to the stables of the stallions, which as I have said are on the right on entering, we made our way to the paddocks, where the mares were out feeding. Practically all of them were being attended to individually by a syce, and I was informed that for the task of attending to the animals a staff of forty syces is maintained, apart from the riders and head lads. Prominent among the mares in the paddocks was Farida, mother of Balance, and all those malicious tongues which wagged and said that Balance was a country-bred need only look at Farida, and then see the sire, to realise that all they said was, as the Americans would say, 'all Hooey'.

Then came a pretty sight. In a large paddock beyond that in which the mares were feeding were half a dozen colts. Here Dr. Ashoub became the spokesman of the party and told how the training of the youngsters was commenced. This is kept strictly to the lines adopted by the Bedouins. As soon as the colt is weaned from its mother it is put into the paddocks with the others, in the centre of which is a large barn. Twice in the morning and once in the afternoon the colts are put to active exercise. This consists of running around the paddocks and is motivated by one of the syces taking an old tin can, in which there are half a dozen pebbles or so. This is shaken vigorously and the resultant noise has a most amazing effect on the colts, who dash around the paddock in fine style. As they came sweeping up from the bottom corner it was a grand sight, heads flung high, manes flying and tails up. To watch them was alone worth making the trip. On the other side of the road is the fillies' paddock, and the same method is also practised for them; exercise twice in the morning and once in the afternoon.

After this we went to the stables where the mares foal, and where all mares due to foal are placed. This is some distance away from the rest of the paddocks and is entirely surrounded by a high wall. Inside is plenty of deep soft sand, and the position of the yard ensures plenty of sunshine. The first thing we saw inside was a foal seven days old sucking from its mother. Tame enough so far as Dr. Ashoub and the syces in charge was concerned, both mother and foal proved much too shy for a stranger to approach. A picture was obtained of this, but unfortunately both were chestnuts and the two were not very distinguishable. In answer to a query Dr. Ashoub said that the Society were happy to be in a position to state that mortality amongst foals is less than one per cent. This, of course, comes about from the hygienic conditions in which the foaling boxes are maintained, and also from the fact that no outside animals are allowed on the farm, thus bringing with them disease, which would have a disastrous effect on the Society's work.

Wending our way back we paid a prolonged visit to the stables of the mares, thirty in number, and one and all came in for admiration. Farida made a splendid subject for photography, but Ibn Bint Sabha was a little troublesome and required no little patience. Bint Dalal, a lightish dapple grey, who was certainly not left behind when good looks were being handed out, also made a fine picture.

Even at the Society's studs the same fee is charged, and thus Balance, who is at Gezira, serves mares for the same fee. It will thus be seen that the predominate idea of the Society is the improvement and encouragement of breeding, and not merely the financial benefits that could be derived. The question of leasing colts is left to the General Committee of the Society, and at present they have five three-year-olds which they are prepared to put out on lease. To encourage the average farmer the Society works in close collaboration with the Horse Breeding Commission.

The average of breeding at Kafr Farouk is about twenty foals yearly, and of those over seventy per cent prove successful either as stallions or mares. Never before have they managed to obtain such a magnificent specimen of the Arab as Balance, and the Committee are already studying ways and means whereby it may be possible to produce others of his type. Ibn Rabdan has been responsible for some good ponies and horses, but they have fallen far short of the standard set by Balance. Two of Ibn Rabdan's stock on the race courses at present are Reall and Rabdan. The sire is over eighteen years old and has been at stud for twelve years, but is still very fertile.

It was with a certain amount of regret that I left the farm as the visit had proved to be highly instructive, as well as most interesting, and at the time of leaving I made a promise to myself that I would repeat the trip at a future date.

A visit to the Sidi Salem Arabian Stud by his Excellency Fouad Abaza

During the last quarter century the local breeding in Egypt of the Thoroughbred Arab (i.e. Arabian Horse) has undergone many vicissitudes, and although it is not the object of this account to resuscitate past history, but rather to deal with the present important role breeding plays in this country, it should be borne in mind that Egypt is an important area for the production of the accepted true Arabian, and that this position has been attained principally through experience gained and handed down by some of the famous establishments no longer existing, but still exerting a strong influence on present-day breeding.

In this connection, one may recall the Sheikh Obeyd Stud, so carefully tended by the late Lady Anne Blunt, whose stock has long since been transferred to England where it is still producing for Lady Wentworth. Then, of more recent day, the renowned Arabian mares so jealously guarded by the late H.S.H. Prince Kemal el Dine, whose progeny found its way into the principal breeding centres in other parts of the world. These, which may be termed Royal mares, for their blood is priceless, have now been distributed between two important studs in Egypt, and it is the one having secured the cream of this stock which I would make my principal theme.

For close on thirty years it has been my privilege to be closely acquainted with the important owners and breeders of Egypt, but these, for the most part, have been interested mainly in the matter of producing horses for the purposes of racing, and, therefore, having not maintained that high standard of strain so necessary in the pure Arabian. It is interesting, however, to know that the Arabian still occupies the attention of those who realise the value of true blood, and who are versed in the intricacies of strain necessary to the obtaining of progeny at all worthy of their predecessors, such as the Darley Arabian, and others of old time.

During the course of my peregrinations recently through the Gharbia Province in the Delta of Egypt, I took the opportunity to pay a visit to Mr. T. G. B. Trouncer, of whose stud I had heard, but never seen. And as he specializes in the pure Arabian only, I was more than interested in the prospect of seeing the exceptionally fine mares he possesses. These include some of the Royal mares already mentioned, who are all of the purest strains, with unimpeachable pedigrees.

Before proceeding to describe the impressions I received during the course of my visit, it was of interest to learn that Mr. Trouncer's present hobby is traceable to circumstances which took him to Arabia and Iraq, where the Arab horse is seen in his native environment, thus affording him wonderful opportunities of acquainting himself with the finer points of the various strains in their natural home. Since that time Mr. Trouncer has been applying his knowledge to practical purposes, and his valuable broodmares have already produced progeny which promises to equal the best Arabs yet seen in Egypt.

I had motored a number of miles through the rich agricultural lands of the Delta and was surprised when I came to what looked more like an English farmhouse than anything else, its immediate surroundings being laid out with long shady avenues resembling country lanes in England and it was in this pleasant setting that Mr. Trouncer was following his hobby in a scientific manner with every evident sign of success.

In giving what must of necessity be a very short description of some of the animals comprising the precious stud, I would point out that when tracing the descent of an Arabian, it is always the direct female line which takes preference over the tail male, the line blood of the dams being everything when considering quality. Thus, one will find in Arabic literature repeated references to Sons of Mares, and such having a decidedly more important signification in so far as quality is concerned than if designated as Sons of Horses, this, of course, being the direct opposite to the manner in which pedigrees of English thoroughbreds are considered.

The first acquaintance I made was the 19-year-old mare called Hegazieh, broad of girth and of beautiful proportions, her head being typical of the type so often heard of, but rarely seen out of its native haunts, Koheilet El Ayala, in the Nejd country.

Interesting history is attached to this mare, who was originally the property of King Hussein. This monarch, it may be remembered, abdicated in favour of his son, Emir Aly, and went to Cyprus, taking with him two mares and two stallions. An unfortunate episode there, however, resulted in one of the mares and one stallion being killed, while the two remaining were sold, the mare eventually finding her way into the Sidi Salem Stud. Since covered by Ibn Rabdan a stallion belonging to the Royal Agricultural Society of Egypt, this mare produced a colt, who, as a yearling, shows signs of becoming an excellent specimen of his race. Hegazieh is now in foal to Gharbour, another of the same Society's stallions.

I was then shown what is considered to be the finest young Arabian mare in Egypt; Rasalla, a delightful 6-year-old bay. This is one of those purchased from the late Prince Kemal el Dine's Stud at Saft, and is by Rustem, who was imported from Lady Wentworth's Crabbet Arabian Stud, and is out of Sit Serra, a Seglawien Jedranieh of the Ibn Sudan strain of the Roala tribe, which makes Rasalla a most valuable acquisition.

The 17-year-old mare named Sit Serra was then brought out for my inspection. Bred by the late Lady Anne Blunt at her 'Sheikh Obeyd Stud', Sit Serra was renowned as being one of the best mares in the Land of the Pharoahs, and passed into the possession of the late Prince Kemal el Dine, from whom Mr. Trouncer was fortunate to purchase her, Sit Serra has since been covered by the champion, Iram, an Egyptian Government stallion imported from Lady Wentworth's Stud.

I then saw a graceful grey 4-year-old daughter of Sit Serra, by Rustem, and therefore, a full sister to Rasalla, whom she greatly resembles in conformation and general characteristics.

The last of the older generation was another grey 12-year-old mare, Shereifa, who I was given to understand is a great favourite with all connected with the stable, being everything that may be considered gentle and docile, albeit exhibiting all the qualities of an excellent brood mare. Shereifa was accom-

panied by a prancing 2-months-old colt, as full of fun as his dam was docile.

The younger generation now growing up in the ideal surroundings provided for them in the capable hands of Mr. Trouncer, should be of undoubted satisfaction to this genial breeder, as Sherif, who then came to my notice, a full brother to the colt just mentioned and whom I omitted to say was by Gharbour, has already earned fame by securing 1st prize in a 2-year-old class at the Ministry of Agriculture's Horse Show, held at Tanta, on the 29th April, 1932, when he was adjudged the Champion of the Show.

I was also shown some other youngsters who should soon follow in Sherif's footsteps, two of which are out of the afore-mentioned Shereifa. The first was a yearling colt named Wazir, whose sire is Gazelle, and the second a nice 2-year-old brown filly called Emira, by Kasmeen, both sires being from the Royal Agricultural Society's Stud.

A third was a yearling chestnut colt, Talal, out of the famous Hegazieh mare

Nazeer (Mansour—Bint Samiha). Painted for the Egyptian Agricultural Society by Judith E. Forbis

by Ibn Rabdan, also a Royal Agricultural Society stallion. These are all products full of quality, and well worth the pains taken in their breeding.

Coming to the last and most recent addition to the Sidi Salem Stud, it gave me real pleasure to see Registan, who is a valuable stallion imported into Egypt from England, where he was bred by Lady Wentworth at her Crabbet Arabian Stud. He is a Koheilet El Ajuz, out of Riz, by that renowned sire, Skowronek, the winner of many championships and the sire of champions. Registan is now a 5-year-old grey, full of Arabian characteristics with a showy style, so his presence in the stud should make itself felt within a year or two, and, I esteem, with excellent results.

As a contrast to other Stud Farms breeding Arabs for racing in Egypt, and which, for the most part, are in the hands of those who have not had the opportunity of studying breeding in the scientific manner so imperative to the best results, Mr. Trouncer's Sidi Salem establishment is undoubtedly a model of perfection and, with its spacious accommodation, roomy paddocks and natural advantages, there is little doubt but that, in the course of time, there will spring from its midst many more champions like the one which has already given the lead.

There came a period of decline both in numbers and quality of the horses bred by the State, and in 1939, Dr. Ahmed Mabrouk of the Royal Agricultural Society, making a survey of the situation after seeing the various Stud Farms, offered some valuable observations and advice:

Breeding the Pure Arab Horse in Egypt by Dr. Ahmed Mabrouk, Head
of the Animal Breeding Section, Royal Agricultural Society of Egypt.
Written for the Arab Horse Society's Journal in 1939

The history of the Arab horse in Egypt tells us that great interest in the breeding of the pure Arab horse has been shown by the rulers of Egypt as far back as the thirteenth century, when considerable success was achieved. It was, however, in the reign of Abbas Pasha I that the reputation of the Egyptian Arab horses reached its height. Abbas Pasha I procured the best examples of pure Arab horses and brought them to Egypt. It was from this stable that the Egyptian bred Arab horses became famous all over the world.

When this famous stable was dispersed the breeding of the pure Arab horse was continued in Egypt by Ali Pasha Sherif, H.H. Prince Ahmed Pasha Kemal, H.H. Abbas Pasha II, H.H. Prince Mohamed Ali and Lady Anne Blunt.

As time went on three of these famous studs were dispersed, leaving that of H.H. Prince Mohamed Ali, who continued his grandfather's famous breed of horses until recent years.

In 1908 the Royal Agriculture Society of Egypt first took a hand in the breeding of the Arab horse, and with the idea of introducing vigour, energy and robustness into the Egyptian horse inbred with English stallions. The result was not altogether a success. The half breds were vicious, ugly and lacked most of the best features of the Arab horse.

It was consequently decided to secure Arab pedigree stallions which were very rare in Egypt; in fact, as my report shows, difficult to procure with any certainty in the East.

At that time the best pedigree horses in Egypt existed only at the stables of H.H. Abbas Pasha II, H.H. Prince Mohamed Ali and Lady Anne Blunt.

In 1913 a few pure-bred mares and horses were obtained by the Royal Agricultural Society from these stables and others imported from famous stables in England. In 1919 the Society bought 20 horses from Lady Went-worth. From that time on breeding by the Royal Agricultural Society was very successful. It is the intention of the Society to persevere until they reach a standard when Egypt will be recognised the world over as the breeding place for the purest bred pedigreed Arab horses.

For some time the Royal Agricultural Society strongly opposed taking outside blood into their pure-bred Arab stock. This subject was discussed at many Committee meetings, and it was at last unanimously agreed that if the pure pedigree bred horse is continually inbred a position would be created where there would be 'all pedigree and no horse'. Experience has shown that continual inbreeding produces a deterioration of quality, and that the introduction of new pure blood is essential. Establishments interested in breeding the pure Arab horse all over the world are convinced of this fact. For instance Poland, Hungary, Russia, America—in fact every country interested in the pure-bred Arab horse —have been compelled to go to Arabia to seek good outside blood of Arabian horses to introduce into their stock.

My recent journey to Arabia and Syria was for the purpose of securing pure thoroughbred Arabian animals to infuse new blood into the stables of the Royal Agricultural Society, thereby continuing the valuable work undertaken by the Society. I met with many difficulties. To my surprise no stud books were available, consequently it was not possible to select animals with any degree of certainty that they were thoroughbred and pure Arabs.

This difficulty has persisted for many years. In a report of a journey under-taken some years ago by Mr. Brown he says: 'after an extended search we found no horses of outstanding merit and excellence in the Irak region and the horses of Homs, Hamma and Aleppo were all of the same order. We finally gave up the search in despair'. Even as far back as 1875 the difficulty of finding pure blood stock was experienced. The sole result of Major Upton's two year trip to Arabia was the purchase of one mare—Naomi—then in foal.

Notwithstanding these great difficulties the finding of new blood is essential, for if inbreeding is allowed to go on without the infusion of new blood the pure Arab horse, which has been famous for centuries, will disappear in a limited number of generations, giving place to an inferior breed of animal which will lack the stamina, courage and handsome appearance of the original breed.

It is some consolation to me to know of the failure of so many missions searching for suitable new blood, even in better times than prevail today; times when good Arab horses were more plentiful, better bred and preserved than is the case today.

Even H.H. Prince Feisul would not give me a certificate of authenticity for any imported animal. He recognised only the Nejd horses bred by himself and his relatives. These are comparatively few and the majority are not suitable for exportation owing to their not being sound, to old age, undesirable markings, etc.

Although the search for the pure-bred Arab horses upon whose pedigree and breed absolute reliance can be placed, is hedged around with so many difficulties, I am by no means discouraged. My journey leaves me with the conviction that by an extended tour and a careful search I should be successful in discovering the pure-bred animal which is so essential to the carrying on of the work of breeding the pure Arab horse in Egypt. The purity of pedigree will depend solely on the decision of the buyer.

My work in Arabia was considerably assisted by the valuable help rendered by H.M. King Abdel Aziz Saoud, who displayed great interest and sympathy in my mission and especially in the recommendation of H.H. Prince Omar Toussoun.

I found, during my journey, that the pick of the Arab horses are sent to Egypt where they are in demand for racing. The good prices they procure when sold and the substantial race prizes are the attraction.

CONCLUSIONS

The Arab horse was at one time generally admitted to be the best for all purposes, without rival in any part of the world. The close sympathy which existed between the Bedouin and his horse, coupled with the free unrestrained life it led, was to a large extent responsible for its excellent characteristics. I do not mean by this that the Arab horse was untrained; on the contrary, he was subjected to a very strict course of training, but of a different character to that of today. The Arab horse was a member of the Bedouin family in every respect of the phrase. A bond of sympathy existed, the like of which has never been seen before or since, and the horse, with this high standard of intelligence, responded to this treatment.

If the Arab horse is bred under any other circumstances he will in time lose all the characteristics of the thoroughbred, viz, if well fed and sheltered he will lose endurance; badly or unsuitably treated, he will lose the even temper for which he is noted; loosely bred without sympathetic handling and contact, he will lose his courage, which will be displaced by a nervousness.

The change will, of course, not take place at once, but steadily as the changed conditions are imposed on the animal in generations.

It is interesting to recall that in 1912 an International Society for the Preservation of the Arab Horse was formed in Egypt under the patronage of H.H. Abbas Pasha, the Khedive of Egypt, with H.H. Prince Mohamed Ali as President and Prince Youssef Kemal as Vice President; other illustrious names connected with the scheme were Prince Alexandre Sherbatoff, the famous Russian horse breeder, and Prince Kemal el Dine Hussien. The first Article of the Society's Charter detailed that the Society was formed in Cairo for the preservation of the pure Arab horse which is absolutely necessary for the amelioration of every other kind of horse in the world, the Society noting the change in the mode of living of the Bedouin and the deterioration of the Arab horse which must follow this change.

Since that time vast changes have taken place in the position and future of the Arab horse. The state of affairs foreseen by the International Society has not only come to pass but has been aggravated by other incidents, such as the Great War, disease, starvation, mechanization of transport and an even more rapid change in the Bedouin habits than was anticipated.

The Great War unfortunately interrupted the activities of the International Society, but if we are to save the Arab horse from complete extinction some action must be taken without delay.

There are still many spheres in which the Arab horse can be valuable such as racing, riding, etc.; and the use of the pure Arab horse for cross breeding is indisputable. To produce for instance the best cavalry horse, hunter, etc., the pure-bred Arab stallion is essential.

It is necessary for Governments who are interested in the production of good class horses for specialised work to step in and make generous donations to a recognised Institution or Society; for the wealthy classes to lend a hand in the great work. Horse breeding, and especially that of the Arab horse, is an expensive matter, generally beyond the means of even a wealthy individual. That is why we must look for a combination of efforts and resources.

So far the work has been confined to a few who have spent lavishly in their endeavours to preserve and improve the breed. Were it not for the efforts of the Royal Agricultural Society in Egypt, Lady Wentworth in England, the Kellog Institute in America, the Hungarian Government and Count A. Dzieduszycki in Poland, we should not have the few fine specimens of Arab horses we have today.

Immediate united action is imperative; delay will only add to the difficulties. The necessity for the preservation of the Arab horse is beyond all possible doubt.

Dr. Ahmed Mabrouk's observations, and his advice have been implemented by the Egyptian Government.

The State Stud (Egyptian Agricultural Organization) formerly The Royal Agricultural Society, founded in 1898, is still carried on in its original establishment at Ain Shems.

The organization of the Stud Farm is based on the concept of the former Director, General Tibor von Szantner (1949–1959), and continued by his successor Dr. Mohammed Marsafi, who had assisted the General. Dr. Marsafi, who is now Director of Animal Breeding has another veterinarian, Dr. Khalil Suleiman to manage the Stud under his direction.

Three Stud Books have been published. Volume I (Royal Agricultural Society) records pedigrees from 1898 to 1952. Volume II (Egyptian Agricultural Society) from 1952 to December 1965 and Volume III from January 1st 1966 to December 31st 1970. The Stud Books of the Society do not record Arabians bred or owned by private individuals, nor does there exist any State responsibility for them, but there are certain 'supervised' Studs, the purity of whose stock is recognized by the Society.

One department of the Egyptian Agricultural Organization is devoted to breeding a racing-type Arabian. A stallion of unauthenticated pedigree, named 'Sharkasi', was bought from the late Mr. Trouncer after a very successful career. Put to pure-bred mares the offspring inherited his speed and stamina, and were much sought after by racing enthusiasts. His son is now the leading sire at the Racing Stables.

Once a year, in November, a public sale of young stock is held.

The purebreds at the State Stud number approximately 300, of which 90 stallions serve at breeding centres throughout the country to improve the native stock owned by farmers.

After the political revolution of 1952, the large estates were broken up and the land re-distributed. The leading Stud Farms owned by the Princes and great landowners thus disappeared, and in many cases the horses were seized by the authorities then in power.

Today, there is little encouragement for the private breeder to establish a Stud as a hobby. There is no home market for the pedigreed Arabian, except as a racehorse, and here purity of bloodlines and conformation are of secondary importance to speed and stamina.

One privately owned Stud Farm, through the courage and single-minded devotion of its owner, survived the troubled years, and built again when it seemed as if a life's work had been destroyed.

This is the Hamdan Stud at Tahanoub, a village north of Cairo, founded in 1942 by Mr. Ahmed Hamza, whose stock ranks in purity and excellence with the best at the State Stud.

The foundation stock was purchased from the late Mr. T. G. B. Trouncer; from the Inshass Stud of the late King Farouk; from the Egyptian Agricultural Society, and from certain Bedouin tribes of Arabia.

The horses bred at this establishment exhibit the traditional classic type and quality with very little variation.

'Hamdan', in whose honour the Stud was named, came from the Inshass Stud. He is described by his owner as 'Our most famous and beautiful stallion, whose blood permeates our herd today'. Hamdan descends in tail female from Horra I of the Saqlawi Jedran Ibn Sudan strain and traces to the Ali Pasha Sherif—Blunt horses, Feysul (Ibn Nura ex El Agraa), and Ghazala El Beida (Ibn Sherara ex Bint Helwa).

The foundation mare of the Hamdan Stud is the exquisite grey Mahasin, now aged 26, bred by the late Mr. Trouncer. She, too is a Saqlawieh Jedranieh of Ibn Sudan, and is Crabbet-bred on her dam's side, with the addition of one cross to Skowronek. Like Hamdan, she descends from Horra I.

Mahasin aged 27 (Sheik el Arab—Kasbana); owned by the Hamdan Stud; bred by Mr. Trouncer

A recent visitor to the State Stud, Mrs. Judith Forbis, describes the horses to be found there today:

There are many descendants on the Egyptian Agricultural Society's farm tracing in the main to Abbas Pasha, Ali Pasha Sherif, the Blunts, and a few other Royal family imports of note, as well as a very few of private breeder imports. These present-day horses are descended strictly from these original authentic Arabs. They are completely different in type from those found on the Egyptian tracks today. Many of the Egyptian race horses have been imported from Iraq and other Mid-Eastern countries and are definitely crossbreds.

There are two or three horses which have been used at the Society for breeding race horses, or rather siring race horses, and their pedigrees cannot be authenticated in comparison to the others mentioned above. The horses sired by these animals are sold in Egypt for racing purposes, to obtain revenue for the farm, and are not used in their breeding herd.

With regard to original Crabbet purchases by the Egyptians in September 1920, those horses which have contributed to current breeding programmes there are: Bint Riyala, Bint Risala, Kazmeen (Sotam—Kasima), Hamran (Berk —Hamasa), and Rustem. The former two mares have considerable progeny in tail female line; the stallions have also been influential, Kazmeen and Rustem more so than Hamran. Rustem sired Bint Rustem (ref. Mashhour).

Gamil Manial is not the same as Jamil. Gamil Manial was by Saklawi II, also known as Farhan, and out of Dalal. Jamil Blunt was foaled in 1896 by Aziz—Bint Jamila—an Ali Pasha mare.

Carl Raswan maintained that Jamil Blunt, not Gamil Manial was the sire of Mansour, and that the records had been improperly recorded by a clerk who thought that Jamil Blunt was too old to sire any more. However, none of the other Egyptian authorities—Dr. Branch, or Prince Mohamed Ali—chose to have the records corrected, if indeed they were incorrect. The spelling of the two names is different only because of dialect differences. The hard 'g' is used in some areas, the soft 'j' in others.

I do not know of any descendants of Ibn Yashmak on the farm today.

Of the Bint Yemama blood-lines, Nasr sired H.H. Mohammed Ali's Hamida (ex Mahroussa). Gamil Manial sired Aziza (ex Negma). Ibn Samham sired Zarife (ex Mahroussa). Ibn Rabdan sired Fadl and Masroufa (ex Mahroussa).

Ghazala el Beida was foaled in 1896 by Ibn Sherara ex Bint Helwa, bred by Ali Pasha Sherif, purchased by Lady Anne Blunt in 1897, sent to Crabbet in 1909, and purchased by Spencer Borden the same year and shipped to America. She was one of the great matriarchs of American-bred Arabs.

Feysul was by Ibn Nura ex El Argaa—bred by Ali Pasha Sherif in 1894 and owned by the Blunts. He sired Radia—one of the most beautiful Egyptian mares. She was out of Ghazala el Beida.

There are many fine Arabians in Egypt at the Egyptian Agricultural Society of the purest breeding in the world. Within the last ten years Egyptian-bred Arabians have been sought by many European countries, and to a greater extent in the U.S.A., for the refinement they impart to their stock.

The best specimens are still those which trace in one or more lines to the old Abbas Pasha and Ali Pasha Sherif horses, and thus carry on the pattern of breeding followed by the Blunts.

It is rare to find a pedigree that does not end with some of the names that are the hall-mark of purity and classic breeding; Astraled, Ridaa, Ibn Nura, El Argaa . . .

ROOT MARES LISTED IN ROYAL AGRICULTURAL SOCIETY VOLUME 1 STUD BOOK (Egypt)

KHEDIVE ABBAS PASHA HILMI II

1 Obeya
2 Shamma
3 Bint Obeya
4 Bint Hadea El-Saghira
5 Bint Gamila

HIS HIGHNESS PRINCE YOUSSEF KAMAL

6 Nafaa El-Saghira

LADY A. BLUNT

7 Radia 'Ghadia'
8 Jamila
15 Durra

LADY WENTWORTH

9 Bint Riyala 'Risama'
10 Bint Risala 'Raziah'

PRINCE MOHAMED ALI

11 Farida
12 Aroussa (over $\frac{1}{4}$ Blunt through sire and dam)
13 Gamila Manial ($\frac{1}{2}$ Blunt)
14 Dalal (over $\frac{1}{4}$ Blunt through sire and dam)
16 Saada ($\frac{5}{16}$ Blunt through sire and dam)

ROOT STALLIONS LISTED IN ROYAL AGRICULTURAL SOCIETY VOLUME 1 STUD BOOK (Egypt)

KHEDIVE ABBAS PASHA HILMI II

1 Fantoum
2 Ibn Halabi
6 Faris

HIS HIGHNESS PRINCE YOUSSEF KAMAL
  3   Ibn Kawkab (25% Blunt)

PRINCE MOHAMED ALI

7	Massoud	32	Hadban, related to Blunt stock
26	Rabdan, related to Blunt stock	33	Mabrouk Manial
27	Ghazal	34	Bark
28	Garboe, related to Blunt stock	35	Kawkab, related to Blunt stock
29	Seil, related to Blunt stock	36	Sader, related to Blunt stock
30	Tayyar, related to Blunt stock		
31	Gamil Manial, related to Blunt stock		

LADY A. BLUNT
  4   Jamil

LADY WENTWORTH

8	Zeidan	17	Karun
9	Samir	18	Bustan
10	Besheir	19	Ras El Mal
11	Rayyan	20	Keslan
12	Nawab	21	Kamar
13	Razaz	22	Kazmeen
14	Raseed	23	Hamran
15	Solajan	24	Ibn Yashmak
16	El Borak	25	Mabruk Blunt

MISCELLANEOUS

5	Shour	39	Kroush
37	Kheir	40	Akram
38	Haroun	41	El Nasser

OTHER ROOT SIRES INCLUDE

El Dere
Michaan
Nabras

Ghandour
Gamal El–Din – all racehorses of
    unknown pedigree

also:
Registan
and

Zareef – both of Crabbet and Blunt
    lines.

Chapter II

Germany

IN THE highlands of the Swabian Alb of south-west Germany stands the Park and the picturesque buildings which comprise the ancient Stud of Weil Marbach. In 1967 Marbach celebrated its 150th anniversary.

The history of the Stud as a centre of Arabian breeding begins at Weil, in the Neckar valley near Stuttgart, when in 1817 King Wilhelm of Wurtemberg, convinced of the supremacy of the pure Arabian as a breed, and its influence in the improvement of all other breeds, imported the foundation stock from Arabia.

The first importation consisted of seven mares and two stallions selected for the King by Baron von Fechtig.

The stallions were Tajar and Bairacter, both Seglawi Jedranis. One of the mares was Murana I, a Seglawi mare of great beauty who was destined to play an immortal part in the history of the Stud.

In 1819 eight stallions and twelve mares were purchased from the Bedouins for the Stud by the Russian, Count Wenceslas Rzewusky, who had spent two years in Arabia, and from this time began the systematic breeding of pure Arabians. Bairacter proved a most successful sire. Of his sons and daughters thirty-seven mares and seven stallions helped to establish the fame of the Stud. He was succeeded by his son Amurath. Other stallions were imported from time to time, the most notable being Gormousch Bournu, Seglawe, Sultan Mahmud and Mameluke.

In 1861, the Stud consisted of fifty-one mares of which eight were imported, all the rest being descended from Bairacter.

To provide an outcross, the white fourteen-year-old stallion, Ghadir, was purchased in Egypt at the Cairo auction of the Abbas Pasha Stud. He is described as being 'of rare symmetry, with a head of the noblest type' and as having been one of the most successful and most prized sires of the Abbas Pasha Stud.

In 1929, the Egyptian bred stallion Jasir was acquired from the Stud of Prince Mohammed Ali. Jasir, by Mabrouk ex Negma, was full brother to Kafifan, descending in the female line from the famous Jellabiet Feysul, and thus of the same descent as the Abbas Pasha–Blunt stock. Kafifan by Mabrouk (Farhan–Tarfa) out of Negma (Dahman el Azrak–Bint Yemama).

In 1932, the Weil Stud became State owned and was transferred to Marbach, near Stuttgart. The high quality of the Weil Arabians has been carefully guarded.

The senior stallion at Weil-Marbach today is Hadban-Enzahi (Nazeer—Kamla),

OVERLEAF:
(above left) *Hadban Enzahi (Nazeer—Kamla); imported from Egypt. Picture taken in 1955*

(below left) *Hadban Enzahi. Aged 16. Picture taken in 1968*

(above right) *Nabuch (Daikir—Nadja)*

(below right) *Sahmet (Hadban Enzahi ex Jatta) mare bred at Marbach*

Mali (Hadban Enzahi—Malacha)

bred at El Zahraa by the Egyptial Agricultural Organisation. He belongs to the same sire line as Jasir, that of Ali Pasha Sherif's famous Saglawi I.

A younger stallion who is proving his value as a successful cross with the Hadban-Enzahi daughters is the handsome Rustan (Witraz—Rasima), bred in Poland. He is a Hamdani Simri of the Crabbet line of Sobha.

The majority of the mares in the Stud today descend in unbroken tail female line from the finest of the foundation mares, Murana I.

There are also descendants of the original stallions imported, Bairacter, Amurath and Gormousch Bournu.

Today, among the finest individuals at Marbach, the following trace to Blunt and Crabbet stock.

STALLIONS

Hadban Enzahi (Nazeer—Kamla). Nazeer's grand-sire was pure Crabbet through Kasmeen and Berk.

Mali (Hadban Enzahi—Malacha). Malachi descends from Kasmeen, who appears twice again in Mali's pedigree.

Nabuch (Daikir—Nadja). Nadja is by Nazeer out of Nefisa, whose grand-sire Hamran II is 50% Crabbet.

Saher (Ghazal—Sahmet), Sahmet by Hadban Enzahi ex Jatta.

Chapter 12

Holland

IN HOLLAND, the finest Arabians are of pure Crabbet blood and are to be found at the Rodania Stud, founded by Dr. H. C. Houtappel in 1937.

It began with the importation of the fine dark brown stallion Rythal (Shareer—Rythma) bred at Crabbet.

The next importations of Crabbet stock, were the mares Tehoura (Radi—Niseyra), and Sulka (Naseem—Nurschida) bred at Hanstead, mares with exceptionally beautiful heads, and the lovely grey Ziada (Fayal—Raxina).

Two important Crabbet-bred additions to the Stud were the internationally

Elzunia (Witraz—Elsa) mare bred in Poland, imported by the Rodania Stud

famous horse Nizzam (Rissam—Nezma), and Noran (Oran—Nerina).

Both Tehoura (through her dam) and Nizzam (through his sire) carry the bloodlines of one of the finest of Naseem's sons; Rissam (Naseem—Rim).

Noran is the sire of Achim (out of Tehoura); a very impressive young horse.

Of the younger mares, Elzunia (Witraz—Elsa), an import from Poland, takes precedence. This beautiful mare, winner of championships, has three crosses of the Crabbet-bred Rasim in her pedigree.

OPPOSITE PAGE:
(above) *Nizzam (Rissam —Nezma), stallion bred at the Crabbet Stud, imported by the Rodania Stud*

(below) *Achim (Noran —Tehoura) stallion bred at Rodania*

Chapter 13
Hungary

HORSE-BREEDING has been carried on in Hungary for at least 2,000 years. It is a land of horses and horsemen.

The earliest type native to the country was the small, tough Pannonian, deriving from the Tarpan, represented today by the Carpathian mountain pony.

The Turkish invasion and occupation of the land from 1526 to 1686 with the introduction of horses of Eastern origin, had considerable influence in changing the type. The result of this infusion of Eastern and some Spanish blood was a sturdy, but elegant 'Hungarian horse', standing about 15 hands, and equally suitable for riding, or work on the land.

In the period that followed the Arabian appears to have been recognised as a breed superior in itself and the most desirable for the improvement of native stock. Stallions brought into the country by private individuals were used on the part-breds, and thus a type developed with more marked Arabian refinement.

The wars during the reign of Queen Maria-Theresa, brought horse breeding in Hungary to a very low ebb, both as regards the number and quality of the horses. In fact, it was impossible to obtain sufficient horses for the army, or for the agricultural needs of the country.

In 1785, when the country was once more prosperous, a State Stud was founded at Mezöhegyes for the purpose of supplying the Austro-Hungarian army with remounts. The scheme, which gained the support of the Emperor Franz Joseph, was put forward by a Captain Csekanics, and the policy envisaged was the production of medium-sized horses for the cavalry, and a heavier type for the artillery. Foundation stock was a mixture of Thoroughbred, Anglo-Norman, Spanish, and Oriental blood.

In 1789, another Stud was founded for the same purpose at Bábolna. The foundation stock came from Mezöhegyes and the breeding policy was the same.

In the years that followed, the history of Bábolna epitomizes the history of the Arabian in Austria–Hungary.

In 1816, the use of pure Arabian stallions on part-bred mares was introduced as a definite policy at Bábolna. Six Oriental stallions were imported from France, and two, Ebhan and Siglavy Gidran, and the mare Tiffle, were bought in Trieste, by Baron Fechtig. Gidran and Tiffle's descendants are still to be found at the Stud.

In 1836, the Commandant, Baron Herbert, visited Syria and brought back seven stallions and five mares. One of these stallions was the pure-bred 'Shagya',

whose name would be forever associated with this Stud through the fame of his descendants. Shagya stood at Bábolna for a very short time before being transferred to another establishment, but when the excellence of his progeny was realised, his sons were acquired whenever they became available.

Arabian mare, by Kuhailan Zaid out of Mersuch II, bred at Bábolna.

In 1842, Baron Herbert bought a further nine stallions and two mares in the Middle East, and in 1856 Colonel Bruderman, later to succeed Baron Herbert as Commandant, organized yet another expedition to the Middle East, with the encouragement of the Emperor, and purchased sixteen stallions and fifty mares. The fourteen in-foal mares all produced foals. This was the first importation of any size where the mares exceeded the stallions in number, indicative of the future policy of increasing the number of pure-bred, rather than part-bred Arabians.

Of this importation, two stallions and sixteen mares, all white, were sent to Lipizza; fourteen stallions and thirty-two mares were allocated to Bábolna. One of the stallions, Akil Agha, was the ancestor of a line which is still to be found there.

Between the years 1879 and 1901, six stallions from the Middle East were imported; Gazlan, Siglavy, Baghdady, Mersuch, the black O'Baijan, and Koheilan.

Of these the last founded a line which became famous throughout Europe.

In the years following the First World War there was an interchange of pure-bred stallions with Poland, Germany, and Yugoslavia, but no outside blood was imported until 1930, when the stallion Ajeeb (Skowronek—Alfarouse) was purchased from England.

In 1911 there were thirty-two private Studs in Hungary, some of which owned stock bought from Crabbet, but Bábolna remained the largest centre for the breeding of pure- and part-bred stock of the highest quality, to serve the needs of the country.

At the same time the greatest consideration was given to the conservation of the pure Arabian blood-lines.

The horses bred here fall into three categories:

(a) Original full-blood Arabian; horses imported from an authentic source of pure blood.
(b) Pure-bred Arabian; horses bred in Hungary from sires and dams whose ancestors can with absolute certainty be traced back to (a).
(c) Arab Race; part-breds, the product of mating pure-bred stallions with mares in whose pedigree are strains of Hungarian, Spanish, Thoroughbred, or any other blood.

It is interesting to note that certain families bred at Bábolna for more than a century, and classified as part-bred Arabians, often display more quality and type than many of the pure-breds. Undoubtedly this is due to rigid selection and breeding on scientific principles.

All the Bábolna stock are branded when young. The brands applied to each breed, or sub-division are distinct, and are placed differently, so the possibility of mistaken identity or breeding is practically impossible.

Given the advantage of a peaceful political climate, Austria–Hungary might have become one of the great centres of Arabian breeding in Europe.

The succession of wars, revolutions, and secessions which has divided this great country, has continually disrupted or demolished the long-term plans of the Studs, both private and State-owned.

Bábolna Stud still remains the oldest centre of pure Arab-breeding in Hungary, and one of the oldest in Europe, but its greatest contribution to equine history is not the pure-bred Arabian, but two families of Arab Race. The Shagya, and the Lipizzaner. They have been line-bred with such success for two centuries that they are now considered an Arab-type breed in their own right.

At the present day there are not above forty pure-bred Arabians at Bábolna, but the importance of conserving this valuable nucleus is realized, and will no doubt be used to the best advantage by this nation with its great tradition of fine horses, and horsemanship to match their excellence.

Chapter 14

Jordan

THE ROYAL JORDANIAN STUD possesses some of the finest stock of classic Arabian type to be found anywhere in the world.

The Stud was founded by the late King Abdullah of the Hashemite Kingdom of Jordan. His Majesty was a renowned horseman, and had the inherited knowledge and appreciation of the true Arabian horse of the desert.

Before his untimely death in 1951 he had collected horses of such superlative quality that today their progeny are still the best, in a Stud where all are good.

H.M. the late King Abdullah reviewing British troops

Bahar; the Senior Stallion, bred by King Abdullah at the Royal Jordanian Stud

Farha (Selman—Mashalla I) aged 20. 'The Queen of the Stables', bred by King Abdullah

The bloodlines are a combination of English, Egyptian, Spanish and desert-bred stock. Many of King Abdullah's horses were gifts from foreign rulers and princes, but only the best of these were retained in the Stud, which, at his death, comprised 50 Arabians of the choicest blood and conformation.

Among these was a grey stallion named Ushaahe (Arabic)—Almozaber, in the Spanish Stud Book—who had been presented to the King by General Franco. Foaled in 1942, he was by Ifni ex Duquesa, both sire and dam bred by the Duke of Veragua. Ifni's dam was Reyna (bred at Crabbet) who was by Skowronek ex Rissla.

Ushaahe sired the best stock in the Royal Stud. His get were consistently good, and perhaps the most successful results were obtained when he was crossed with the daughters of the Egyptian-bred Selman (Al Fajar) Mansour ex Sabaah in the Egyptian Stud Book. Ushaahe is the sire of those fine stallions El Thabi (now in the U.S.A. – owned by Douglas Marshall) and Al Bahar, the leading sire in the Royal Jordanian Stud. Farha, a mare of superlative beauty and presence is by Selman—Mashalla I, bred by King Abdullah and traces back through the sire-line to Abbas Pasha stock.

After the death of King Abdullah, the Stud and its upkeep became of secondary importance to other more urgent affairs of State. Many horses were given away

Amapola   (Madrid—Mashalla II)

OPPOSITE PAGE:
(above) *Gazella, and foal Mahbuba by Bahar*

(below) *Gazella and foal Asila*

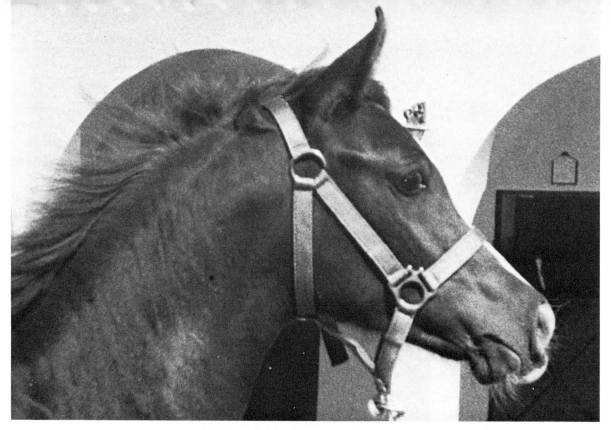

Farida (Bahar—Farha) filly, aged 6 months

Baharein, colt (Bahar—Samiha)

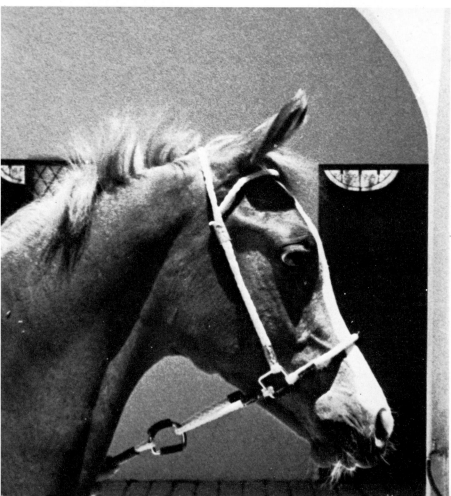

and some put into training for the race course. In 1953, King Abdullah's grandson, *Bahar aged 15*
Hussein, came to the throne.

King Hussein in 1962 decided to re-establish a breeding programme in keeping
with the Royal tradition of the past while maintaining the Stud under modern
standards.

Jordan, by virtue of its climate, terrain and geographical position provides
highly favourable conditions for the breeding of the pure Arabian. Today there
are 200 horses at the Royal stables. Of these only the choicest are selected for the
Stud. The rare Kehaileh el Krushieh strain is preserved in the mare Gazella, and
her daughter Amapola. Other strains represented are Seglawi Jedrani, Hamdani
Simri, Kehailet Ajuz, Abu Argub, and Kebeysha.

The horses are kept in modern stables in beautiful surroundings.

Farha, the truly Royal mare now more than twenty years old, has handed on
the legacy of beauty to her daughters Samiha, Mashalla, and Kerima, yet, she
remains the Queen of the Stables.

Chapter 15

Poland

IN POLAND, as in no other European country, the Arabian has been the favourite breed for centuries; 'the horse of Poland' as much as 'the horse of the desert'.

In this largely agricultural land, the Arabian was valued for certain qualities which made him particularly suitable for his environment. To the small farmer the Arabian was appreciated for his equable temperament, thriftiness, soundness and adaptability to work on the land or for transport.

The great landowners vied with each other in the acquisition of the most beautiful specimens of the breed; indeed Poland before the First World War could have justly claimed to possess some of the finest and most classically bred Arabians in the world, with a lineage as old as history.

Three famous Studs, owned by wealthy and dedicated breeders, Prince Roman Sangusko at Slawuta, Count Joseph Potocki at Antoniny and Count Xavier Branicki at Uzin carried on the royal tradition of breeding Arabian horses. Their original stock was of the choicest desert breeding, or from the Ali Pasha Sherif in Egypt.

The Slawuta Stud dated from the year 1506. The original stock being reinforced periodically by further desert imports.

In 1802, Prince Hieronym Sangusko sent his equerry Burski to Arabia. He returned two years later with five stallions (two of them were Gniady and Janczar—Aga) and a mare.

In 1816, the older Sangusko's son, Prince Eustachy, sent his equerry Mosznski to Arabia to obtain the best horses he could find. Mosznski with the help of an Englishman named Rawson who, with his Arab wife lived in Aleppo, selected and brought to Slawuta in 1818, nine stallions and a mare. Among the former were: 'The white Hajlan', a Kehailan bought in Damascus for 3,500 frcs. who became a very notable stallion; the grey Dzelf bought in the Babak desert; the chestnut Dzedran, from Hama; the bay Seglawi from the Swira desert, and the brown Obejan bought in Aleppo.

In 1821, another band of desert-breds chosen by an Arab agent named Aratin came to Salwuta, among them the grey mare Gazella. But the best stallions ever exported from Arabia were Batran-Aga and Abu-Chejl.

Batran-Aga, a Seglawi Jedran, grey with a dark mane and tail, was bought by Prince Roman Sangusko in Aleppo in 1844. There was opposition to this sale from the Viceroy of Egypt who offered to buy him from the Prince rather than

Argos (Nabor—Arfa)

allow him to leave the country; after two years of negotiation Batran-Aga finally came to Slawuta. Batran-Aga sired the stallions Iskander-Bazza, from whom descended the mares Perta, Latka, Kreolka and Obehan-Macznik.

Another horse that added fame to the Slawuta Stud was the stallion Abu-Chejl. He was a grey with dark mane and tail, a Seglawi-Jedran, reputed to be the speediest horse of the tribe, bred in Syria. He was acquired with great difficulty by Count Julius Dziednszycki in 1845, and sold to Slawuta in 1854.

Abu-Chejl crossed with Batran-Aga's get produced outstanding stock. One was the mare Melpomena, who in 1900, won the Gold Medal at the World Show in Paris. But probably the best stallion from the Abu-Chejl family was the grey Rymnik bred in Slawuta in 1876. Rymnik, bred to Lira, the daughter of Epopeja (from the Batran Aga family), produced Yaskolka, dam of Skowronek.

In 1881 the two great Studs of Slawuta and Antoniny were merged through the inter-marriage of the two families.

The Blunts visited these Polish Studs, and Count Joseph Potocki, Senior, was a frequent visitor of the Blunts at Ain Shems. Mr. Blunt notes in his diary on the

14th September, 1895, that he had spent the day visiting Prince Sangusko's Stud at Christowka and saw what he describes as 'a magnificent collection of mares'. Though he notes at the same time that neither here, nor at Antoniny were the stallions worthy of the mares.

In the 1890's Count Joseph Potocki bought the stallions Pharaoh and Proximo from the Crabbet Stud. He later sold Pharaoh to the Russian State Stud when they purchased a band of mares from Crabbet. Pharaoh proved himself an outstanding sire while at Antoniny and four of his sons were sold to Turkey.

The Branicki Stud at Uzin imported two colts from Crabbet in 1897, but these perished together with 130 other horses when the Countess Branicka's property and stables were burnt down through the malice of a groom.

Between 1925–1928, Baron Bicker of Pognanski imported from Crabbet the five mares, Karima (Faris—Rusalka), Fasila (Rasim—Fejr), Nitla (Nureddin—Nashisha), Sardhana (Nureddin—Selima) and Ramayana (Nureddin—Riyala);

Nabor   (Negativ—Lagodna)

to complement this band he bought the superb stallion – Champion Rasim. Ramayana was in foal to Rasim, and produced Rasim IV, whose influence is still evident in Polish bloodlines.

The tragedy of War and invasion has haunted this nation of horse loving people. The Antoniny and Slawuta Studs were wiped out by the Bolshevists during the First World War, except for five mares saved from the massacre.

The ferocious slaughter of the horses; assassination of the old Prince Sangusko, and the destruction of palaces containing the Studbook records of the priceless stock which had been garnered for 400 years was a loss to civilization that time cannot recompense.

The predicament in which Poland's Arab-breeding centres found themselves after the Second World War is described in the following paragraphs published in a Polish magazine in 1966:

The Second World War and the Nazi occupation cut short the remarkable development of horse breeding in Poland. The dedication of Polish employees of the Stud farms requisitioned by the Germans, and their admirable devotion to their horses averted an irreparable catastrophe.

Witez II and all the remaining Arabs of the Janow Podlaski Stud were evacuated to the Third Reich in 1945. The horses lived through the massive Allied air raid over Dresden in February 1945. The chronicle of Janow Podlaski records that on the night of terror, J. Ziniewicz, the groom, did not for a moment release his hold on the reins of the two prize stallions Witraz and Wielki Szlem, thus saving their lives in that crumbling city engulfed by a sea of flames. That night, twenty-one of the magnificent Janow Podlaski horses perished at Dresden. Were it not for the fortitude and courage of the Polish groom the casualties would have been incomparably greater.

A vast reparation programme was launched directly after the war. As Polish grooms had remained with the plundered horses, it was possible within a comparatively short time to round up most of the valuable stallions and mares scattered throughout Europe.

The Polish Arab Stud at Janow has developed from fifty-two pure-bred Arab mares which were finally collected. They were returned to the farm as soon as Janow was restored from destruction.

Post-war breeding has been carried on at three Studs; Abligowa in the southeast; Nowy Dwor, between Cracow and the Czech frontier; and Michalow in Central Poland. Recently the horses from Nowy Dwor have been transferred to the famous old State Stud at Janow Podlaski, where many great Arabians were bred before the war, and where there is also a large, old-established Stud of Shagyas and other Oriental half-breds.

Today, a notable contribution to excellence in Polish-bred horses comes from the Skowronek dynasty through his son Naseem. Naseem, bought by Russia from Crabbet, sired Negativ, who sired the Polish-bred Nabor. In the years ahead Nabor may prove to be one of the most significant stallions of our day.

Gerwazy (Doktryner—Gwara)

Chapter 16

Russia

THERE IS evidence that as far back as 1533, in the reign of Ivan the Terrible, horses of Eastern origin were acquired in large numbers, though there are no records of Studs established for the exclusive breeding of pure bred Arabians till 1778, when Count Alexis Orlov founded a Stud at Chrenowje of pure Arabians. These having been sent as a gift from the Sultan of Turkey.

The stallions Sultan and Smetanka at this Stud were renowned for their beauty, and the latter earned the historic distinction of having shared, through the line of Barsz I in the foundation of the renowned breed of Orlof-trotters.

In 1802, Count Rostopotschin obtained from Arabia for his Vorenevo Stud near Moscow, eight stallions and seventy-six mares, and in 1889, another effort to establish a Stud of pure Arabians was made by Prince Scherbatov and Count

Pomerantz (Priboj— Mammoona) chestnut, 1952

Solon (Negativ—Sonata) grey, 1959

Lax (Kancan—Laba) grey, 1960

Arax (Amurath Sahib —Angora) bay, 1952, imported from Poland

Stroganoff, who undertook a journey through Syria and parts of Arabia in their search for the pure Arabian, returning with eight stallions and twenty mares.

From subsequent records it appears that the Arabian blood was used most profitably for the improvement of racing stock; for the breeding of a good type of cavalry horse; and, by crossing with the Orlof-trotter and various native and imported breeds to produce an impressive 'Oriental type' Russian saddle horse like the fine Strelets, the Akhal-Teke breed, and later the Terski strain.

In 1899–1900, the Russian Government realizing the importance of Arabian blood of the finest quality in their breeding projects, purchased from the Crabbet Stud, the great Mesaoud (Aziz—Yamama) together with three of his sons; Anbar out of Queen of Sheba; Naam out of Nefisa; and Rishan out of Rose Diamond.

With these stallions went five mares: Dijleh (Ashgar—Dahna); Jeneyna (Azrek—Jerboa); Makbula II (Wazir—Makbula) and Sobha (Wazir—Selma) of Abbas Pasha.

The catastrophic events of the First World War in 1914, and the subsequent Revolution in 1917 resulted in almost total destruction of both private and State established Studs; their livestock, buildings, and records. After the War, when more favourable conditions had been established, the Government began a programme of reviving the centres of horse-breeding.

Some of the finest Polish stock which had been transferred to Russia for safety during the course of the War still remained there. Arabians were imported from Hungary and France, and in 1936 a Commission was sent to England.

They bought from Lady Wentworth twenty-four Arabians whose influence remains to this day. The most notable stallions were Naseem, a son of Skowronek out of Nasra; Shareer, by Nureddin II—Selma; and Raseem (Rasim—Rim). There were also the colts Jeruan (Nureddin II—Rose of Persia); Rytham (Shareer—Rythma) and Ferhan (Raswan—Fejr). The eighteen mares were: Nasifa (Skowronek—Nasra), Nashisha (Rasim—Nasra), Bisharieh (Naseem—Battla), Rissalma (Shareer—Rissla), Grey Crabbet (Raseem—Silver Fire), Star of the Hills (Raswan—Selima), Rixalina (Raseem—Rissla), Nissam (Raseem—

Naprasalina (Nomer—Plotka)

Naprasalina, head study

Neraida), Najera (Rahal—Nasirieh), Rashifa (Shareer—Rishafa), Ruanda (Najib
—Rythma), Naharina (Nureddin II—Nasira), Neraida (Nureddin II—Nasifa),
Riama (Nureddin II—Dafi), Rimula (Nureddin II—Rimini), Rose of Africa
(Nureddin II—Falila), Ruellia (Nureddin II—Riyala), Silka (Nureddin II—
Somra).

The Second World War disrupted once again the profitable achievements of
Russian horse breeding, but steps were taken to avoid serious loss in the more
valuable stock. More importations from Poland took place towards the end of the
War, and during recent years the stallion Aswan, a son of Nazeer was obtained
from Egypt. The type and classic beauty of this horse should be of great value to
the Russian-bred Arabians. It is of interest to note that he descends largely from
Blunt stock.

With reference to the influence of the early Crabbet imports on the breeding of
Arabians in Russia today, an analysis of pedigrees in the latest Stud Book published by the Ministry of Agriculture in Moscow shows that by far the greatest
influence was exerted by Naseem. His blood carries on through Negativ, Nomer
and Nabor, and altogether 23 of his daughters were used for breeding. The
Skowronek influence is also apparent in the progeny of Ferhan and Star of the
Hills, though not as effectively as Naseem. Of the mares, Rissalma leads in importance, and her half-sister Rixalina was also a notable producer. The leading
sire in Russia today – Pomaranets – is a grandson of Shareer and Rissla.

Chapter 17

South Africa

IN SOUTH AFRICA the importation and breeding of Arabians was sporadic up till 1935. Climatic conditions and insect pests have made it a disheartening environment for extensive rearing of pure-bred stock but with the advancement of scientific methods of agriculture, soil conservation and the eradication or successful treatment of pest-borne diseases, interest in the horse, as indeed of all pedigreed stock, has become a national concern. The registration of all pure-bred stock is scrutinized by the State-controlled South African Stud Book Registry.

Apart from the early importations of 'horses from the East' brought into the Cape Province by the Dutch East India Company, one of the first recorded importations was Merzuk, in 1891 from the Crabbet Stud. He was a chestnut horse, a Kehailan Jellabieh, bred by Ali Pasha Sherif, the dam a Kehailet Jellabieh, sired by Wazir, a Seglawi Jedran of Ibn Sudan. In the same year, the celebrated stallion Azrek, a Seglawi Jedran; one of the desert-bred horses imported by the Blunts, was brought to the Cape by Cecil Rhodes.

The next notable import was Ibn Mesaoud, a chestnut horse foaled in 1892 by Mesaoud out of Saada, bred by the Blunts at the Sheikh Obeyd Stud in Egypt.

In 1908 the first pure-bred Arabians were entered in the South African Stud Book. These were three desert-bred horses. The next year Capt. Gomer Williams imported three mares from Crabbet. They were Malwa (Nejran—Mabsuta), Kesra (Mesaoud—Kurfa) and Nimawa (Mesaoud—Nefisa). In 1910, the stallion Khalikan (Mesaoud—Khatila) bred by Lady Anne Blunt, was imported by a Mr. W. Frost.

Further importations from Crabbet were made in 1918, when a stallion, Faird (Astraled—Fadila), and the two mares Andrina (Rijm—Asfura) and Faud (Daoud—Fadila) were purchased by Mr. W. E. Lovemore.

In the tragic years between the two world wars imports were not possible and breeding had to be restricted by the needs of agriculture, and there is little or no record of how this valuable Crabbet blood was used, or how it affected the Arabians of today, except in the case of Jiddan, imported in 1938 by Mr. Claud Orpen of Avoca. Sired by the Crabbet stallion Sher-i-Kurshid, his dam, Baida, was a quarter pure Crabbet, and three-quarter desert-bred.

Hadban, a famous stallion, one of the early Blunt importations was also purchased by Mr. Orpen at this time.

After a lapse of some twenty-seven years a fresh start was made, again by Mr.

Orpen. In 1945 he imported three stallions and two mares from Egypt. One of the stallions was Zahir described by one who had seen him as 'a magnificent nearly black Arab stallion of classical type', bred at King Farouk's Stud. The mares were Nabilah and Barakah (Ibn Manial—Gamalot) bred by the Egyptian Agricultural Society.

Olford Sylvietta (Royal Crystal—Silverlet) bred and owned by Mrs. E. B. Arnold

Jiddan and Zahir have made a valuable contribution to the blood-lines of present-day Arabians in South Africa, while old Barakah, still beautiful in spite of her great age, has descendants who will be the best testimony to her excellence.

In 1946, Mr. G. D. Kock, of Deelfontein, Cape Province imported three stallions and two mares. From Crabbet, the stallions Indian Gem (Raktha—Indian Crown); Indian Red (Raktha—Nezma) and the mare Nazziria (Naziri—Nezma). From Hanstead, the mare Ghezala (Faris—Rasana) and from Mrs. E. M. Carroll the stallion Rasheen (Irex—Rishka). Later he imported Shahim (Rangoon—Somara) from Mr. W. Hay of Winestead Hall.

The same year W. Van der Merwe of Vlinkfontein imported two stallions bred on very different lines. These were Boaz (Joseph—Betina) bred by Mr. Musgrave Clark of the Courthouse Stud, and Rabiyas (Rahas—Rabiyat) foaled in 1936 and bred by W. R. Brown in America.

Olford Serabelle (Royal Crystal—Serafilla) bred by the Duke of Veragua and owned by Mrs. E. B. Arnold

Bint Razena (Raktha—Zena) bred and owned by Mr. and Mrs. J. B. Grobbelaar

Since 1946 the importation and breeding of Arabians has increased in a spectacular manner. In 1951, the first Arabian Championship Show sponsored by the Arabian Horse Breeders Society, was held in Graaf Reinet with barely a dozen pure-bred entries, though there were many more part-breds and Anglo-Arabs. In 1966, there were 150 entries from every part of the Republic.

The horse whose blood-lines dominate the South African scene is Raktha, that great son of Naseem, bred by Lady Yule in 1934 at Hanstead, and later acquired by Lady Wentworth. Mr. A. J. Botha imported Raktha in 1952, a loss to England as enormous as it was an advantage to South Africa. Raktha was then aged eighteen.

At the Middleburg Show held in the Cape Province the following year, he was Grand Champion Arabian, but before that there were already in the country, sons and grandsons of this famous horse, themselves Champions and siring Champions.

Today, there are no fewer than four Champions by Raktha, six Champions by his son General Grant, and one by another son, Rithan.

As a result of these early imports of fine bloodlines, the Arabians bred in South Africa today in the leading Stud Farms are of a very high class. They differ somewhat in type, which is understandable when one considers the various strains to which they owe their origin; moreover, the older establishments have bred within certain lines, as much from necessity as from choice, since distances are too vast for any easy exchange of stallions.

Three leading breeders have contributed much to the establishment of newer Studs.

The Jamani Stud at Villiers in the Orange Free State, own some high-class imported stock bred by Lady Yule at Hanstead. Headed by the stallion Grant-chester (General Grant—Rafeena) Mr. and Mrs. J. B. Grobbelaar have a superb band of mares which includes Zena (a daughter of Queen Zenobia), Correze (sired by Count Dorsaz), Garance (Grey Owl—Rikitea), Bint Razeena (Raktha—Zena) and Reibara Rakitee (Raktha—Garance). Besides the pure-breds, the Grobbelaars have been most successful in the production of Anglo-Arabs and part-breeds. In the 1966 Championship Show held at Bloemfontein, horses bred at this Stud won for their exhibitors, twelve Firsts, four Seconds and seven Thirds, two Championships and three Reserve Championships.

Mrs. E. B. Arnold's Olford Stud at Olivefontein in the Cape Province has Arabians of somewhat different blood-lines. She owns two most valuable Crabbet-bred horses. Champion Royal Crystal, a grey stallion of dazzling magnificence by Ch. Dargee out of Supreme Ch. Grey Royal. The senior brood mare is Silverlet, by Raktha. She is one of the few daughters of that lovely mare Silvergilt, who is also the dam of Silver Vanity. Silverlet was imported in 1948.

Since then there have been other imports and many fine horses bred from this stock. To mention but a few, Serafilla (Raktha—Sharfina); Dancing Crystal

Jamani Shah Burak (Al Burak—Reibara Shala); bred by Mr. and Mrs. J. B. Grobbelaar

(Royal Diamond—Dancing Star); Irexina (Irex—Yavroum), all three Crabbet mares, and the young stallion Raktha Scha (Raktha—Schadilla), bred in South Africa.

Mr. and Mrs. T. E. M. Murray of Graaf-Reinet, Cape Province, have a comparatively small, but most important band of Arabians at their Roode Bloem Stud.

Two mares were imported from Hanstead in 1950. The chestnut Kumara (Grey Owl—Hama), and Kasala, a grey (Sala—Queen Zenobia).

Kumara, who was exported in foal to General Grant, produced a beautiful colt, the well-known Major Grant, who became the Stud's senior stallion.

Kasala was imported in foal to Blue Domino and produced a filly, Timarie Blue Sala who has added greatly to the lustre of the Stud. She is a Champion herself and the dam of many prize-winners. In 1969 at the National Championship Show she crowned her career when her daughter Timarie Grey Shadow, owned by G. A. R. North, became the National Champion mare; her son Timarie Captain Silver, owned by Victor V. Voorendyk, was National Champion Stallion, and Blue Sala herself was Reserve Champion to her daughter. Both Timarie Grey Shadow and Timarie Captain Silver were sired by Major Grant and thus line-bred to Raktha.

The Raktha blood has been reinforced with the acquisition of the stallion Chief Kasalo (General Grant—Rikitea) to succeed Major Grant. This magnificent Hanstead-bred horse had won the Supreme award at the Arab Horse Society's Show in England before he came to South Africa.

Mr. Victor V. Voorendyk, President of the Arab Horse Society of South Africa owns the 1969 National Champion Stallion, Timarie Captain Silver. The Stud's Senior Stallion is Chez-Nous Shah Rukh (al Burak—Silsilla) a horse with a perfect head and neck. Both stallions carry Raktha blood. The Senior mare Silsilla (Rithan—Somara) was imported from Crabbet, and there are some very fine home-bred mares bearing the prefix of the Stud, Vidiko, such as Vidiko Blue Grass (Chez Nous Shah Rukh—Nazrina), champion mare at the Rand Show 1969. This Stud has also bred very high-class Anglo-Arabs and part-breds.

Mr. and Mrs. G. A. R. North have a beautifully situated farm, 'Blue Waters', in Somerset West on the slopes of the Helderberg mountains. This small Stud has the distinction of owning two National Champions. The chestnut Shalwan (Silver Vanity—Shalina) was chosen on a visit to Crabbet when he was a yearling; and in 1966 as a five-year-old he had grown into a horse of outstanding quality and was awarded the Stallion Championship.

The National Champion mare, Timarie Grey Shadow, mentioned earlier, is

Timarie Captain Silver (Timarie Major Grant —Timarie Blue Sala); bred by Mrs. T. E. M. Murray; owned by Mr. Victor Voorendyk

Chez Nous Shah Rukh stallion (Al Burak—Silsilla); owned by Mr. Victor Voorendyk

also owned by the Norths, and the two charming mares, Jamani Jenni Lee, and Jamani Cora Lynn.

Another farm situated in a perfect setting is the Sahibi Stud owned by Dr. Valerie Noli-Marais. The estate lies on the slopes behind Table Mountain, bounded on two sides by the Tokai Forest with a beautiful view towards the hills of Somerset West.

The foundation stock of this comparatively new Stud have been chosen from an interesting variety of blood-lines. The senior stallion is Zingari, sired by Zahir, one of the stallions imported from Egypt in 1945 by Claud Orpen. Reference has been made to Zahir earlier in the chapter. Zingari has twice won National Championships under saddle.

The senior mares are all imported. Rosina (Saoud—Ruth), bred by H. V. Musgrave Clark; Indian Pearl (Oran—Indian Flower), Crabbet-bred; Indian Glory (Dargee—Indian Pride) Crabbet bred; Suleena (Irex—Nouronnihar) bred by Mr. K. W. Cumming and Dusty Dawn (Desert Dust—Dawn Shadow).

Very recently Mrs. Noli-Marais bought the old mare Barakah, yet another of the Egyptian imports of 1945, and though now over twenty years old her owner hopes to obtain another foal from her.

This is a thoughtful experiment in the influence of blood-lines, the result of which could be valuable in the future.

There is a link between the Sahibi Stud and that of Gordonville, Eersteriviere, Cape Province. Here Mr. Ian Thompson keeps his stallion, Gordonville Ziyadan, a son of old Barakah by Zingari's sire, Zahir.

He also owns the former National Champion stallion, Boaz (Joseph—Betina), bred by Mr. H. V. Musgrave Clark, imported in 1946. He has a good mare in Olford Silver Mist (Silver Rocket—Silverlet) of Crabbet blood, who has produced an outstanding daughter by Ziyadan.

Other breeders who are contributing to the high standard of Arabians in the country are Mr. and Mrs. J. Kettlewell, of the Jerico Stud, Mount Stewart, who own a former National Champion, the imported stallion Sikander Shah (General Grant—Garance) bred at the Well House Stud, and an excellent band of mares.

Mrs. E. M. Chapman of Lions Bay, Natal. The Chapmans have been in touch with the Arab world for many years, and were among the earliest overseas members of the Arab Horse Society in England.

Timarie Lady Mae (Captain Kidd—Kumara); bred by Mrs. T. E. M. Murray; owned by Mr. and Mrs. Weilbach

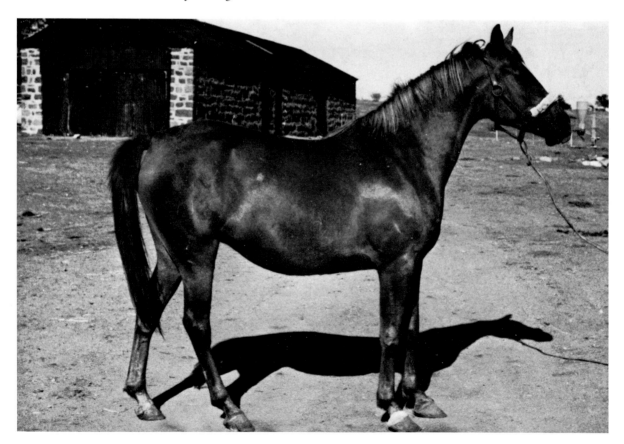

Reibara Raktha's Sou-
venir (Raktha—Silsil-
la); bred by M. C. Nel;
owned by Mrs. A. R.
Weilbach

The largest Studs in the country are owned by farmers; horse-breeding is only part of their wider farming interests.

The long-established Agricultural Shows include classes for horses of many breeds and of great variety. Once dominated by the famous country-bred Boer-perde (Farmer's horse); a very good type akin in looks, stamina, and temperament to the American Quarter-horse, and famed for the speed and comfort of his 'trippling' gait.

The Shows are now on so vast a scale that they can extend for a week, and every day has a full programme. They are the 'shop-windows' of the farmer and the industrialist and provide a happy opportunity for meeting old friends and making new ones, since exhibitors come great distances from every part of the country.

Classes for horses include the Thoroughbred, American Saddlebred, Hackneys, teams of heavy horses driven to farm wagons, Boerperdes, Ponies, Anglo-Arabs, and in increasing numbers, the pure Arabian. Arabians (including Part-breds and Anglo-Arabs) also have exclusive Championship Shows every three or four years.

In the Agricultural Shows each breed has its own ridden class, but there are also Open competitive classes for the best Riding horse, from which only the registered Saddle-bred is excluded. In these Open classes the well-schooled Arabian is beginning to make his mark both in hack classes and in the three, and five-gaited classes.

Four Arabians who have won outstanding success in these classes are, Dancing Wings (bred at Crabbet, owned by Mrs. E. B. Arnold) a brilliant performer who won three successive Championships.

Raktha Scha, owned and bred by Mrs. E. B. Arnold, and the mare Timarie Blue Pride, bred and owned by Mrs. T. E. Murray.

The imported Crabbet-bred Sun Brilliant (Oran—Silindra) was another who made his mark as a five-gaited horse.

Basically, in South Africa there is still the inborn love of the horse. The farmer, or the executive, has his huge glistening car, but more often than not, tucked away in the stable is a beautiful horse.

The South African as a connoisseur of the horse can hardly be excelled, and that he has realised as a breeder of fine horses the potential value of Arab blood, as exemplified in the class of Anglo-Arabs, show-hacks, part-breds, and excellent ponies to be seen all over the country today.

Chapter 18

Spain

SPAIN IS a country well suited in climate and terrain to the breeding of Arabian horses, where they have long been used for the cavalry, for pleasure, and for transport. Today there are several private Stud Farms with highly selective breeding programmes. The Casa Belalcazar owned by the Countess Belalcazar; The Yeguada Ybarra, owned by Don Jose Maria de Ybarra; The State-owned Yeguada Militar – the largest of the breeding establishments; and one other which will be more fully described later – the Duke of Veragua's Stud Farm.

Up to the outbreak of the Second World War, stallions were imported whose bloodlines are still a major influence in the excellence of the stock bred today in Spain. The impressive grey Baghdad, desert-bred and imported in 1927 – Nowick, also desert-bred; and Korosko, bred in Egypt and imported in 1912.

Scanderich, another great sire, was desert-bred; Ursus came from the Branicki Stud at Kiev, and Van Dyke (Vasco da Gama—Hela) from Poland.

Between 1926–1930 the Duke of Veragua made the greatest contribution to the

Reyna (Skowronek— Rissla); bred in England at Crabbet Park; owned by the Duke of Veragua

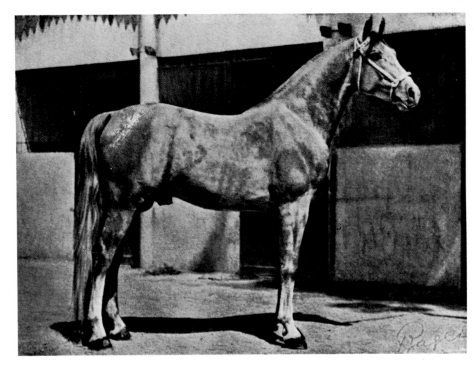

Razada (Shahzada — Ranya); bred by C. W. Hough

breeding of Arabians in Spain when he imported a band of eight mares of the finest bloodlines to be found, from the Crabbet Stud. They were: Amusheh (Rasim—Arusa), Insilla (Naseem—Nisreen), Ranya I (Nasik—Riyala) and five daughters of Skowronek. Jalila out of Rasima; Namira out of Nessima; Nasieda out of Nasra; Reyna out of Rissala; and Shelifa, out of Selima.

The worth of such mares as individuals, and their potential value to breeders in Europe is impossible to estimate; yet this treasure was to be scattered in the Civil War of 1936, and records of their lineage destroyed. In September 1936 the Republican Government decided to take possession of all livestock belonging to the Spanish aristocracy; the Duke's Stud Farm at Valjuanete, near Madrid was taken over by the Ministry of Agriculture, but the horses were not removed immediately. A few weeks later the Republican troops arrived to occupy the property and demanded that the stables in which the stallions and some mares were housed should also be handed over, together with the horses. The Duke would not consent and the rabble shot him dead, then killed the grooms who like their master, had stood firm in their resolve not to yield the horses in their care. The mansion was set on fire and many irreplaceable books, documents, and all the Stud Records destroyed. Seventeen Arabian stallions and thirty-three mares lost their lives or disappeared. However, the brood-mare band, with their foals, and the young stock were on the uplands where they grazed across

Alhama III (Congo—Galatife) mare bred in Spain of Veragua stock

the river that ran through the estate. This the Republicans did not know. A month later, General Franco, hearing of the devastation, sent troops to rescue the remaining horses. They found thirteen colt-foals, and forty-six mares and fillies, including four of the Crabbet mares, Jalila, Namira, Naseida and Reyna. These were all taken to the Yeguada Militar.

While there could be no possible doubt as to the purity of breeding of the Veragua horses, all of whom were branded with a 'V'; and the identity of the older horses could also have been certified; the difficulty arose in establishing pedigrees of the youngsters when all Stud Records had been destroyed. To trace the individuals of pure Abbas Pasha–Blunt breeding would now be impossible, many of the foals were by Razada who had been imported and widely used at the Veragua Stud. It has been incorrectly stated that Razada was bred at Crabbet; in fact only his dam Ranya was of Crabbet breeding; his sire was Shahzada who was by the imported horse Mootrub out of Ruth Kesia, a mare bred by Miss Dillon and tracing back four generations to El Emir.

The loss of the Veragua Stud Records was a tragedy for Spain. The devotion and knowledge of the Duke had produced a band of Arabians of beautiful type and precious lineage. Individuals bred at this Stud have, in the last thirty years, gone to enrich other breeding centres in Spain; their names have the prefix 'Vera' and, since the sire cannot be named, it is simply stated 'From the Duke of Veragua's Stud Farm', which is accepted as a guarantee of purity.

Chapter 19

United States of America

A FOREWORD BY JAMES P. DEAN

THERE WERE many importations which furnished the foundation or background for what we know, and the world is beginning to accept, as the American Arabian horse. Those who have seen Arabians in other countries of the world will most readily recognise this type difference.

In almost fifty years of observation, many conclusions begin to take form and shape but none are more forcefully apparent than that our hindsight is much more illuminating than our foresight.

The Arabian importations of the twenties and thirties and earlier were not greatly different from the other good light horses of that time, which when we think of it, were composites of horses from other parts of the world and practically all originated from some Arabian background.

It was not until the introduction of the blood of Skowronek through his imported sons and daughters in the late twenties, that the type of the Arabians began the trend toward what it predominately was in the 1960's.

Since the fountainhead of Skowronek blood was at Crabbet Park it is not illogical to assume that the Crabbet importations exerted the greatest influence on this early development of a more uniform classical type.

Due to the wide distribution of the imports throughout the U.S.A. and the difficulties of early transportation and, most notably, the lack of comprehension among the breeders of the time as to what was taking place, the transition in type was necessarily slow.

My greatest regret in life is that I, or some other breeders, did not know how to make the best use of the direct sons and daughters of Skowronek which were available to us in the 1920's, 1930's and 1940's.

Most of the credit for what we might consider the Skowronek type which is the most desired in America today is given to his sons, yet I know now that we did not make anything like the best use of the great daughters of Skowronek which were brought to this country.

It will be interesting to note, but only time can tell, whether the type founded on these great bloodlines can be preserved as we get further and further from Skowronek, the fountainhead of excellence in the early Arabian importations.

While it is not the purpose of this book to describe in detail the virtues of any particular horse or the successes of his breeder, it is of importance to record the names of those who, by their forethought and wise selection imported horses of pure Abbas Pasha–Blunt bloodlines *which have contributed most* to the excellence of the Arabian breed in America today.

Spencer Borden, Interlachen Stud, Fall River, Massachusetts

The first import of historic importance was made in 1905, when Spencer Borden acquired the mare, Rose of Sharon by Hadban out of Rodania one of the most famous foundation mares at Crabbet. In 1906 he imported another important mare, Rosetta, (Mesaoud—Rosemary). Rose of Sharon was in foal to Harb when she came, and produced Rodan, sire of Gulnare out of the Ali Pasha Sherif mare Ghazala, imported from Egypt in 1909. Gulnare was the dam of Gulastra.

Abu Farwa (Rabiyas—Rissletta)

Dunes
(Ferneyn—Fersara)

W. R. Brown, Maynesboro Arabian Stud, New Hampshire

In 1918 several valuable horses were brought into the country by W. R. Brown. Judged by their progeny the most important were the stallions Berk (Seyal—Bukra), sire of Ribal, Roshana, and Nardina, and the mare Rijma (Rijm—Risala) who was the dam of Rizvan (by Ibn Yashmak) imported in utero, and of Ribal and Raad.

Rizvan later sired Bahreyn, Nadirat and Gharifet. Other mares imported at this time were Baraza (Razaz—Bereyda) dam of Bedawi. Ramin (Berk—Rim) dam of Ramghaza and Rehal, and Felestin (Ibn Yashmak—Fejr), dam of Kashmir, and Kishta.

The importation of Berk was of special significance when one considers his pedigree and the value of his bloodlines in England and America today. He was the grandson of Azrek, a desert-bred Seglawi Jedran imported by the Blunts. Lady Wentworth records that Azrek was noted for his brilliant action. We find the same comment recorded by those who saw Berk in action; and today this brilliance is found in the progeny of his sons and daughters who themselves inherited it. The names of his daughters – Rythma, Rangha, and the incomparable Rissla are found in the pedigrees of the finest English Arabians today, especially those noted for their action. Rissla being the dam of Rissalix who sired the champions, Ranix, Mikeno, Blue Domino, and Count Dorsaz, and grand-dam of the internationally famous Raffles.

The Maynesboro Stud deserves a special place in history for the foresight which acquired from Homer Davenport the important stallion Aby Zeyd (Lal-i-Abdar) bred at Crabbet, by Mesaoud—Yemama, and from Governor F. Lathrop Ames of Massachusetts that great horse Astraled (Mesaoud—Rose Diamond).

Pomona Ranch, California

Founded and owned by Mr. W. K. Kellogg. In 1926 he imported a band of seventeen Arabians of pure Crabbet blood, whose value can hardly be over-estimated. Raseyn (Skowronek—Rayya) and Nasik (Rijm—Narghilch) were two of the finest stallions bred at Crabbet at the time.

Raseyn founded a dynasty of his own. Of the 134 progeny listed in the Stud

Count Dorsaz (Rissalix —Shamnar)

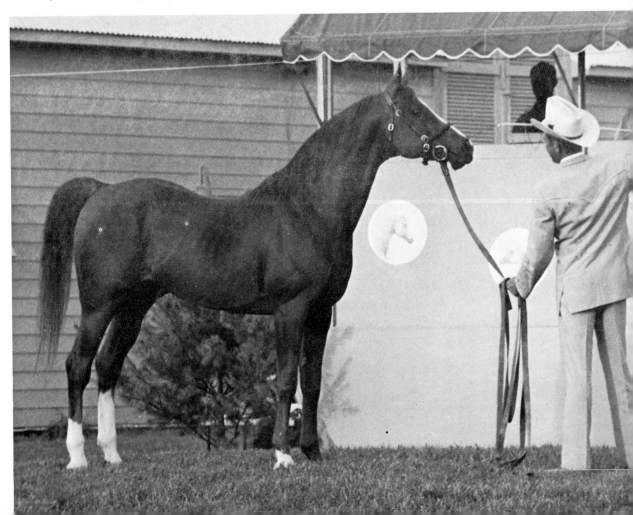

Ferzon
(Ferneyn—Fersara)

Books up to 1937 the one who has brought most fame to his illustrious sire is surely Ferseyn, son of one of his mares imported at this time, Ferda (Rustem—Feluka). Today, thirty years later Ferseyn still heads the list of sires of champion progeny. Ferda also produced two very good daughters, Ferdisia, by Rafeef, and Ferdeyna, by Raseyn.

Other noteworthy sons of Raseyn are, Ronek, ex Bahreyn; Ferdeyn ex Ferdisia; Moneyn, ex Monica; Famhuri ex Ferafa; Sureyn ex Crabbet Sura; Sauwid ex Incoronata; Gohara ex Rosanna; Ibn Raseyn ex Zahara; and Echo ex Rifnetta.

Raseyn's famous daughters are too numerous to list but those deserving of special mention are: Rasrah ex Kirah; Rasoulma ex Malouma; Raweyna ex Sherlet; Ralouma ex Malouma; Rasena ex Menfis; Moneyna ex Monica; Nofa ex Narasa; Roseyna ex Roshana; Nakkleyn ex Nakkla; Daanaseyn ex Raidanna; Freyha ex Kirah; Ralla ex Nakkla; Romona Adagio ex Dirabba; Balena ex Dirabba; Bahia ex Zewa; Rasaleh ex Taleh; Rasewa ex Zewa; So Big ex Chloe; Surra ex Zewa; Angyl ex Wierna; Little Bit ex Chloe, and Talmia ex Taleh.

Nasik, a horse famed for his wonderful action which was inherited by his progeny both in England and America, is credited with thirty-two sons and daughters bred at the Kellogg Stud.

Of these the most noteworthy sons are: Ferdilan ex Ferda; Farana ex Farasin; Rifnas ex Rifla; and Valensik ex Valencia. Some of his famous daughters are: Shemseh ex Rifala; Rossika ex Rossana; Nafara ex Farasin; Ferdika ex Ferda; and Sikara ex Farasin.

Rossana, a grey daughter of Skowronek ex Rose of Hind was imported at this time, and was the dam of Rossika by Nasik; Ferdana by Ferdin and the colts Rossdin by Ferdin; Farasa by Farana; and Gohara by Raseyn.

Another superbly bred mare in this group was Rifla (Rasim—Rim), in foal to Nureddin, she produced Rifda, and later the lovely Shemseh by Nasik. In 1936 three other famous mares were added to the Maynesboro Stud.

Risletta (Naseem—Risshina) a grand-daughter of Rissla. Crabbet Sura (Skowronek—Sardhana) and Incoronata (Skowronek—Nisreen).

Incoronata was the dam of the beautiful mare Sonata. Crabbet Sura was the dam of Ch. Sureyn.

Fadjur (Fadheilan— Bint Sahara)

Johnny Johnston

Gazon
(Ferzon—Scheraff)

The Selby Stud, Ohio

Mr. Roger A. Selby, a well known business man and a lover of horses since boyhood, was the founder of one of the finest Arabian Studs of the century. He was a man of wide experience in the breeding of horses, and fairly late in his career he decided to breed Arabian horses, if he could but find the classic type he admired.

Lady Wentworth wrote a foreword to Mr. Selby's Stud Book which is worth quoting in this context:

Mr Roger Selby's Stud is of the greatest importance, perhaps greater than he himself realizes. . . . It is to America that I look for the energy and foresight to save the Arabian breed and preserve it. Mr. Roger Selby is just the man to see further than most people as to the ultimate value of stock.

Blue blood and beauty are perhaps at a discount in the mechanical world of today, but the world of tomorrow will be a dull place if there is no beauty and no aristocracy of equine stock with which to delight the eye and rejoice the heart — man's heart, for with beauty, symmetry and balance of form are allied comfort, ease and speed. . . . Mr. Selby started with the best blood of Arabia. Nothing better can be found anywhere. He has chosen from the old Crabbet blood and from old stock of the tribes which goes back thousands of years and which has remained unchanged and unspoilt, like the gazelles of the desert, and he will see that no inferior blood spoils its beauty. In improving the riding stock of America by providing the material for crossing, he is doing a great work, but the greatest work of all concerns the preservation of pure blood which he has secured for his Stud and which is its main object.

Roger Selby's first importation of pure Abbas Pasha–Blunt stock was in 1928, when he bought eight horses from the Crabbet Stud.

Among the mares were the greys, Rifala (Skowronek—Rissla) and Kareyma (Naseem—Julnar) and the bays Indaia (Raseem—Nisreen) and Hilwe (Najib—Hafra).

The chestnut stallion Mirzam (Rafeef—Julnar) came with them.

Group of four mares: from left to right, Chloette (Serafix—Chloeyn) Fixette (Serafix—Chloeyn) Silver Dawn (Serafix—Silver Crystal) Starfire (Serafix—Serafire)

Serafix (Raktha—Sera-
fina)

This nucleus would have been sufficient for the founding of a very good Stud when one considers the produce of these mares. Rifala was the dam of Raffles (who was imported later) and of the stallions Image, Rifage and Phantom, and amongst her good daughters was Ragala. Indaia was the dam of the famous horse Indraff (by Raffles).

Other noteworthy sons were Indrage, Dairaff, Athos and Indy.

Her most famous daughters were probably Rafla, Rafaia, Flaia and Raffia.

Kareyma was the dam of the stallions Arabi Kabir, and Ibn Mirage, and the mares Rageyma and Rafeyma.

In 1930 Mr. Selby added to his valuable stock the mares Rose of France (Raswan—Jalila) a double grand-daughter of Skowronek, Selmnab (Nawab—Simriah), Kiyama (Rafeef—Julnar) and Namilla (Nureddin II—Nejmia).

Rose of France was the dam of the mares Rose of Luzon, Selfra, Bride Rose, Romira, and Franza.

Selmnab is remembered chiefly as being the dam of Nurselma, Imna, Nabima, and the stallions Selmage, Nabraff and Idol.

Rasmina, produced two very good sons, Rasraff and Ibn Raffles, and the noteworthy daughters Rahmina, Rafina, Rafmina, and Bint Rasmina.

In 1932, Mr. Selby made the greatest contribution to his Stud and to Arab breeding in America by the importation of Raffles, an inbred son of Skowronek. This little grey horse, standing only 13·3 hands high was destined to be as famous as a sire of classic stock in America as Skowronek was in England. He also acquired Nureddin II, then aged twenty-three, who had been a very successful sire at Crabbet; and the beautiful desert-bred Mirage.

Of later importations the stallions Selmian (Naseem—Selima) and the mare Rishafieh (Jeruan—Rishafa) were the most valuable.

Selmian sired Selfra, Selrisha, Fiehmia, Ishmia and Selmiana. Rishafieh was the dam of the fine stallions Ferishal, Samyn, and Rishan; among her other good daughters were: Selvisha, Fiehmia, Ishmia, Raffieh, Rishra, and Rizieh.

It was a tragedy for the Arabian world when the necessity arose for this famous Stud to be drastically reduced in 1949. Nevertheless, Arabian breeders in America still remember with gratitude their debt to Mr. Selby in the records of Champions of today.

The Rogers Arabian Stud, Walnut Creek, California

Mr. John M. Rogers having spent many years in the East determined to found a Stud of Arabian horses using only such individuals, and such bloodlines, as he considered would perpetuate the desert type with which he was familiar.

When he left Saudi Arabia he took with him to California five desert-bred mares. Very wisely, Mr. Rogers added to this, three mares and a stallion of the finest Crabbet stock. Silver Crystal (Rangoon—Somara) imported in 1951 in foal to Grand Royal produced the champion filly Royal Silver.

Serafire (Indian Magic—Grey Royal) champion, and dam of champions was imported the following year, together with the unbeaten champion Serafix, one of Raktha's finest sons, by Serafina. The success of this group as individuals and of their sons and daughters in the show ring must constitute a record for any breeder.

There are three other well known Stud Farms where the results of selective Crabbet–Skowronek bloodlines demonstrate a consistent uniformity of classic type. They are:

The Manions, of 'Manion Canyon', South Bend, Indiana.

Lodwick Arabian Farms, Williamsburg and Mt. Orab, Ohio.

Dr. W. B. Munson's 'Shalimar' Arabians, Cambridge, Illinois.

The importance to the world of Arabian breeding in America cannot be over-estimated.

The Arabian Horse Registry was incorporated in 1908. Since September 3rd of that year to September 30th 1969, a space of sixty-one years, 56,000 Arabians have been registered.

The Real McCoy
(Aarief—Fersara)

Perhaps as many as ten times more than there are in any other country, indeed in any continent.

To put it simply America is now the largest centre of Arabian breeding in the world.

In contrast with other 'traditional' centres there never has been a tradition of exclusively bred Arabians in the country, of this or that type, or blood-lines, or history.

Rather, America has absorbed what breeders considered the best, of all types, of all bloodlines, from every country.

With the vast resources of this great country, and the complete dedication of so many established breeders, America should become the source of the finest Arabians in the world.

The picture today is an intricate mosaic, of glittering focal points against a uniform and less interesting background.

The earliest Arabians imported brought with them an aura of tradition, which breeders then and now have attempted to perpetuate, but traditions which are based on history and environment can rarely be transplanted to another climate and remain unchanged in some fundamental aspect.

For example, the practice of maintaining a 'herd' of horses is not a genuine tradition of the desert. The vast establishments of Eastern princes and the Royal houses of Europe which set this precedent, were not commercial ventures, but the garnered treasures of connoisseurs. Treasures beyond price, and honour lay in owning them. Contemporary writers seldom recorded the fate of the 'rejects'.

Again, the Arabian is traditionally a riding horse; a fleet-footed horse; a 'drinker of the wind' – above all a horse with the natural floating action which is the hall-mark of his high breeding.

To encumber him with ponderous saddles; to force him to restrain the light thrust of his feet by artificial 'aids', and to make him 'a performing horse', instead of 'an effortless performer under saddle' is a travesty of tradition.

The demands of competitive success in the Show Ring and its weight as an assessment of the value of a horse is a break with tradition.

An Arabian should be judged for his *natural* beauty – beauty that might include white markings, or the tail carried a little to one side; but this method of assessment presupposes a body of judges who are familiar with the natural beauty of an Arabian in natural surroundings. Such surroundings and such judges are a rarity in any country today. So the art of Showmanship must take the place of Nature.

There are two major hazards in this procedure. First, a mediocre horse superbly shown, can be placed above a good one ineptly handled; there are so many con-comitant circumstances that can affect a horse's success in the Show Ring.

Secondly, his Fate, and future, lie in the hands of a judge who would be less than just if he did not assess the horse before him in the light of his own opinion. Yet, how do we assess the judge? Is he the man most breeders would choose to be their agent in the selection and purchase of Arabians in some distant land?

Nevertheless, in spite of disadvantages, Shows are a necessity in any country where horses are bred. There is no better method of comparison within the breed.

The holding of an International Show in America once a year (though strictly speaking the only other nation involved is Canada) is an idea, which if it could be supported and organised to include every Arab-breeding country that cared to participate, a truly International Pageant of the finest specimens in the world, held even once, would be a landmark in Arabian history.

In a continent as vast as America (or countries as far apart as Russia and Spain) there must inevitably be a variation in 'the popular type', depending on the success of a particular horse, which other breeders in that area would seek to emulate; or the ascendancy of horses shown from one breeding establishment.

Amerigo   (Ferseyn—
Syarya)

Whether variation in type within limits is a good thing or not is a debatable point – whether they are good *horses* or not is of the greatest importance. The breed cannot expect to justify its value if it does not conform in essentials to certain standards required of its only rival, the thoroughbred.

So here again we must compromise with tradition. The typical 'horse of the desert' was a frail creature compared with his modern descendant. The argument whether breeding for size is incompatible with breeding for type has never been satisfactorily resolved. How much type? What is the limit of size?

The traditionally beautiful head and eye is the goal of every breeder; yet one most important attribute that is rarely found, and hardly appreciated is 'quality' – an attribute as difficult to define as it is impossible to disguise. Without it there can be no approach to perfection.

It is the outward and visible sign of high breeding in any animal, and does not depend on faultless conformation or show condition.

The result certainly of selective bloodlines, there may also be the influence of environmental factors. The horse that has for generations been treated with respect for his needs and his nature; sensed his master's affection and pride of ownership, would develop a certain mental attitude which could be reflected in his whole personality.

An Arabian is a horse of unique responsiveness and sensitive dignity; he is man's friend. To live as a prisoner, with little human contact, destroys the very essence of his being, his proud 'quality'.

There is one tradition which no circumstance of time, or environment has changed. The most valued stallion or mare, to any breeder, is still that which produces the best stock.

In America there are two lines of breeding which dominate all others in the value of their descendants today. Those of Raffles (Skowronek—Rifala) and Raseyn (Skowronek—Rayya).

Taken still further back in the ancestral line the greatest influence would stem from the great foundation mare Rodania; from Mesaoud (Aziz—Yemama); and from Skowronek.

Royal Storm (Ferseyn—Bint Sahara)

Synbad (Julep—Sahra Su); a grandson of both Gulastra and Indraff

These are the most successful sire-lines judged by the number of champions they have produced (up to 1964):

Ferseyn (Raseyn—Ferda)	all Crabbet breeding
Indraff (Raffles—Indaia)	all Crabbet
Serafix (Raktha—Serafina)	all Crabbet
Witez (Ofir—Federacja)	all Polish
Sureyn (Raseyn—Crabbet Sura)	all Crabbet
Fadjur (Fadheilan—Bint Sahara)	Egyptian, Polish and Crabbet
Rapture (Raffles—Rafla)	all Crabbet
Abu Baha (Abu Farwa—Surrab)	mainly Crabbet
Rifage (Mirage—Rifala)	Desert-bred, and Crabbet

The comparative value of Arabian bloodlines in America is summarised by Gladys Brown Edwards in these words:

The majority of Arabians bred in America, at least those which figure high in today's Show Results, trace in several or all lines to those bred by the famed Crabbet Park Stud of England. Even Polish or Egyptian imports often have a line or two of this blood, from the Crabbet sales to Poland, Russia and Egypt.[*]

* Old Timers, *Arabian Horse World*, January 1965.

Chapter 20

Lady Wentworth

THE FAME of the Crabbet Stud has, in a manner overshadowed the remarkable personality of its owner. The world knew Lady Wentworth as an autocrat whose opinions brooked no contradiction; as the writer of two authoritative works, *Thoroughbred Racing Stock*, published in 1938, and *The Authentic Arabian Horse*, first published in 1945; and as a wonderful tennis player, among the many sports at which she excelled. But perhaps it is not so generally known that she was also a gifted painter, sculptor, writer of poetry, and a photographer whose skill many professionals might envy. Her great sense of humour will always be recollected by those who knew her. The keenness of her mind and her wit are well illustrated by the marginal comments in books and papers she used for study in writing her books.

Portraits of Lady Wentworth in her youth show her extraordinary beauty; in later years one observed as well, her grace and dignity. Her eyes, which were strangely compelling, had the rare brilliance of sapphires; her hands were fine and delicate, and her voice never lost its soft clarity.

During the Second World War a section of the Army was billeted at Crabbet Park, the Officer's Mess being in the house. It has been related how, one evening Lady Wentworth asked her 'guests' whether they would play billiards with her, and having agreed out of courtesy to their hostess they were completely taken aback when she was the overwhelming victor.

When the country was once more at peace an annual social event was established at Crabbet which provided both an education to those who were interested in Arabians and a delightful and satisfying experience to established breeders. This was a parade of part of the Crabbet Stud, some forty to fifty being shown, and took place in the Spring or Summer.

The Parade included young stock, mares with foals, and stallions of all ages. It was faultlessly organised, and staged against a perfect background of green lawns and mellow stone walls. Among the invited guests there were always visitors from abroad as well as local residents; and parties of children from local schools and Pony Clubs. To those privileged to have attended one of these Parades there must always remain a memory of wonderful horses in a perfect setting, a frieze of beauty, colour and movement.

The estate at Crabbet Park, and the welfare of anyone who worked for her were always foremost in her mind; when the age of retirement came she saw that those

Lady Wentworth

who had served her were well cared for, and there were an exceptional number of long-service records among the Stud workers. 'She was like a mother to us all' was the description of one employee recollecting how Lady Wentworth regularly visited her pensioners and the cottages on the estate.

In her last years she retired more and more from the life of the outside world. Her horses and her Stud Farm were her chief preoccupation.

In the great house filled with shadows and memories, she lived almost entirely in the Library with its treasures of books and pictures.

Two little ladies, identical twins, served her in the house, and her devoted Irish maid came daily to see to her personal needs. For the last two or three years of her life she had a Secretary to help her in her vast correspondence and work on her books – a task which became increasingly difficult when her eyes became affected by cataract, for which she had to undergo an operation. Yet her wonderful memory for detail, and her brilliant command of words never failed her.

Her love of horses was the love of a connoisseur for that which is rare and perfect. She once described Arabians as 'having a unique genius for beauty', and these words can perhaps best epitomise the life and work of Lady Wentworth.

Conclusion

THIS IS the chronicle of a tribe of Arabian horses sharing a common heritage, pure in descent and princes in blood. I have traced their history; their journeyings; their vicissitudes; their days of glory and their near extinction.

They travelled, descendants in blood of a band who left the desert, their home-land, more than a century ago. In their pilgrimage they faced disease and poverty; dwelt in cities; were the cause of envy and strife; became the greatest riches of a ruler and the ransom of a prince. Finally they crossed the seas and established themselves anew in that position of honour which the ancient world had accorded them.

Fate preserved their unity, but had it not been for their supreme excellence they would indeed have been a lost tribe today.

In every country where Arabians are bred, the finest claim affinity with this noble band. The future of their legacy is in the hands of the civilization of our day. May it never betray its trust.

MARGARET GREELY

Appendices

THE ARABIAN
by Wilfrid Scawen Blunt

Reprinted from the *Encyclopaedia of Sport*. Published by Lawrence & Buller Limited, 1900.

The Arabian horse – in Arabic 'Kehailan' – is probably the most ancient of existing domestic breeds. He is also the original 'thoroughbred' horse of the East, from whose exemplar all Western ideas of thorough breeding in horse flesh were derived. He has been held in repute as of 'noble' blood for at least 1,300 years, and has been bred with fanatical reverence and pure from all foreign admixture in peninsular Arabia as far back as the records of that country go; that is to say, till the second century before Mohammed, the sixth of our era.

It is a matter of considerable dispute in modern science whether or not the Kehailan was indigenous to Arabia as an original wild breed. The common Mohammedan tradition would make him a gift from Solomon to the Arabs, or, again, descended from mares ridden by the prophet; but Western criticism rightly rejects these tales, nor are they, in truth, real Bedouin traditions local to Arabia itself. The local tradition is that the Kehailan is a separate wild breed kept pure in the desert from the time of his first capture and domestication; that his habitat was Nejd and the high plateaux of Yemen, and that he owes his distinguishing qualities to the fact that his original blood has never been mixed with that of breeds of inferior type. In physical science there is as yet nothing positively ascertained which would show this to be improbable. The high plateaux of Arabia, though all of them desert land – in the sense that they contain no district where crops can be grown in full dependence of the rain fall – are neither without pasture nor without water. It is unquestionable that the wild ass existed, if he does not still exist, in Yemen, and the wild horse too may have there existed. In the sandy tracts there is a certain fine grass called 'nossi', which grows freely, especially within range of the occasional monsoon rains, and it is excellent pasture for horses, so that it is quite conceivable that in the gradual drying up of the peninsula, of which we have geological proof, a section of the wild species may have found itself cut off in the South from the rest of its kind, and have developed there in isolation the special qualities we find in the Kehailan. This is Professor Ewart's opinion, and, in the absence of evidence to contradict it, may be provisionally accepted as true. On the other hand, what historical evidence does exist is adverse to the idea of a very early possession of the horse as a tame animal in Arabia. The Bedouins, certainly of Northern Arabia, would seem during the ages immediately preceding Christ to have been, as indeed many of them are still, exclusively camel-riders, and there is a significant absence of all mention of the horse in lists which have been preserved of the then products of the country. Strabo, on the authority of his friend Aelius Gallus, Prefect of Egypt, who made an armed expedition into Western Arabia in the year A.D. 24, says of Arabia Felix (Yemen): 'The products of the soil are good. Much honey is made and much cattle reared, amongst which, it is true, are seen neither horses nor mules'; and again of the land of the Nabatheans (Hejaz): 'the land does not produce horses, but camels take their place'.

The monumental French work of M. Pietremont, *Les Chevaux prehistoriques et historiques*, should be consulted on this point, his opinion being that the Arabs did not become horse riders till the third century after Christ. In English our best authority on the subject, though perhaps rather out of date, Colonel Hamilton Smith, is of a similar opinion; and on historic grounds alone the balance of evidence would seem to be in favour of a comparatively late date for the domestication of the Kehailan. All that we know positively is that in the fifth and sixth centuries of our era the Bedouins of Nejd and Yemen were already possessed of a special breed of horses of which they boasted as an 'ancestral possession'. 'Are not these,' says their poets of that date, 'an inheritance from our fathers? Shall not we to our sons in turn bequeath them?' It is clear too from their descriptions that the horse then possessed by them was identical in his chief characteristics with the modern Kehailan, as were the ideas of his owners concerning him. There is a description in one of the Abu Zeyd cycle of romances of a Bedouin Mare, which is precise in its details and which might have been written yesterday:

> *Spare is her head and lean, her ears pricked close together,*
> *Her forelock is a net, her forehead a lamp lighted,*
> *Illumining the tribe, her neck curved like a palm branch,*
> *Her wither sharp and clean. Upon her chest and throttle*
> *An amulet hangs of gold. Her forelegs are twin lances.*
> *Her hoofs fly forward faster ever than flies the whirlwind,*
> *Her tail bone borne aloft, yet the hairs sweep the gravel.*

Nor are prose writers silent. Ockley, in his *History of the Saracens*, quotes from the Arab historian, El Wakidi, a decree of the Caliph Omar, A.D. 633, which shows the value already set in Arabia on this special breed. 'After the battle of Yermul,' El Wakidi says, 'Abu Obeidah, the Arabian commander, divided the spoil thus: "To a horseman he gave thrice as much as to a footman, and made a further difference between those horses which were of the right Arabian breed" (which they looked upon to be far the best) and those that were not, allowing twice as much to the former as to the latter. And when they were not satisfied with the distribution Abu Obeidah told them that the Prophet had done the same after the battle of Khaibar, which upon appeal to Omar was by him confirmed.'

Of European authors the oldest I can find mentioning the Arabian horse as a special and valued breed is Marco Polo. He, writing about the year 1290, says of Arabia and the Port of Aden: 'It is from this Port of Aden that the merchants obtain the fine Arabian destriers of which they make such great profit in India, for you must know that they sell in India a good horse for well one hundred marks of silver and more.'

It is certain, however, that long before this the Kehailan must have made his way into Europe, for the first time doubtless in the van of the Arab invasions of the eighth and ninth centuries, which having swept across North Africa, passed over into Spain, and through Spain into France. Here he left his trace permanently in the Barb and the Andalusian, and, as is locally believed, in the French Limousin. The great value, however, of the Kehailan Blood does not seem to have been fully recognised in Europe until the practice of wearing heavy armour in war was well on the decline, and it was then introduced rather through Turkey and the Barbary States than directly from Arabia. Leo Africanus, a Moor of the sixteenth century, who had travelled through the whole of North Africa and of the Arabian deserts from Timbuctoo as far as the Persian Gulf and allowed himself to be converted to Christianity at Rome, makes an interesting mention in his description of Africa of the Arabian horses, which, under the name of Barbs, began at that time to be renowned in Europe, and which is of especial value as showing the close connection between the Barb and the Arab. 'This name (of Barb),' he says, 'is given unto the Barbarie horses throughout Italy and all Europe, because they come forth of Barbarie and are a kind of horse that are bred in those regions, but they who think so are deceived, for the horses of Barbarie differ not in any respect from other horses; but horses of the same swiftness and agilitie are in the Arabian toong called throughout all Egypt, Syria, Asia, Arabia Felix, and Deserta by the name of Arabian horses. Historigraphers affirme that this kind of wild horse ranging up and down the Arabian deserts ever since the time of Ismael have so exceedingly multiplied and increased that they have replenished the most part of Africa; which opinion savoureth of truth, for even at this present there are great store of wilde horses founde bothe in the African and Arabian deserts. And I myself saw in the Numidian Desert a wilde colte of a white colour and having a curled maine. The most certain triall of these horses is when they can overtake the beast called lant or the ostrich in a race; which if they be able to performe they are esteemed woorth a thousand ducats or an hundred camels.' The lant (eland?), he explains, 'is so exceeding swift that no beast can overtake him, but only the Barbarie horse as is beforesaid'. He also affirms that 'the Arabians of the desert take the wilde horse and eate him, but he will hardly be taken with either horses or dogs. In the waters where this beast keepeth they lay certain snares, covering them over with sand, wherein his foot being caught he is entangled and slaine'. The writer of this monograph quite recently received identically the same account as this of Leo's from a negro of Wadai, who spoke of the wild horses still captured there as Kehail. He described the method of snaring them, and declared that when tamed they could go ten days without water. The Arabs of Wadai used them as sires with their tame mares.

In England we first hear of 'Barbs' in Charles II's time, when the 'Royal Mares' were brought for the King from Tangiers, and about the same time of 'Turks', captured in the wars in Hungary. It was not, however, till the beginning of the eighteenth century that the great success of the 'Darley Arabian,' a horse of undoubted Kehailan blood and purchased direct from the Arabs of Northern Arabia by Mr. Darley, our Consul at Aleppo, revealed to English breeders the true source of excellence in Eastern blood. From this date the importations registered in the Stud Book show a constantly increasing preponderance of 'Arabians', as against Barbs or Turks. They were, I imagine, obtained direct from the Syrian Ports or the Persian Gulf; and there is every probability, judging from such portraits of them as remain to us, that they were pure Kehailans, though of the Darley Arabian alone we know the particular strain of blood, Manaki, to which he belonged.

Captain Upton, in his interesting book, *Newmarket and Arabia*, enumerated 101 Arabian Stallions, 44 Barbs, and 28 Turks, as having been registered first and last in our Stud Book. The importation was well maintained until near the close of the eighteenth century, when it seems to have been interrupted by the great war which then began and which made communication with the Levant difficult.

It would be an interesting speculation to calculate the amount of true Kehailan blood flowing in the veins of our modern English racehorse, but it is one on which I dare not enter here, beyond hazarding the opinion that it amounts to at least three-quarters, perhaps to seven-eighths of the whole. It may well be that even the unknown English mares figuring at the head of most pedigrees were in fact partly of this blood, either through Barb or Turk or Spanish ancestors – while in the male line the blood of the Darley and Godolphin Arabians is everywhere preponderant. The Godolphin, although reaching Europe through Tunis, was almost certainly an Arabian, as his original name, 'Scham' (Damascus), would seem to indicate.

The price of Arab horses in the seventeenth and eighteenth centuries seems to have been high. Henry Blount, 1634, says that in Egypt in his day as much as 1,000 pieces of eight was paid for a three-year-old of the true breed; Hamilton, 1720, mentions £50 and £60 as being a small price for one at Moccha; and Niebuhr, 1762, says: 'The English merchant was offered at Bengal twice the purchase money for one of his horses, but he sent him to England, where he hoped that he would draw four times the original price (say £800).' *The Sporting Gentleman's Dictionary*, 1735, mentions still higher sums '£500, £1,000, £2,000, and even £3,000'; as 'intolerable prices' demanded for the 'right Arabian horses' exported from Scanderoon (Alexandretta), pricing at the same time the Turkish horses at £100 to £150, and the Barbs at but £30 in their own countries. In 1782 Arthur Young records that at the Royal Stud at Pompadour in France three Arab horses had just been acquired at a cost to the King of 72,000 livres (£3,149).

In former days the Kehailan was bred in most Arabic speaking lands with more or less purity. Egypt, Syria, and South-Western Persia, to say nothing of the Barbary States, had their own breeds, which boasted of pure Arab origin; but at present the area of his distribution has been restricted even in Arabia itself within comparatively narrow limits, and there are indications of a decline of the race which seems to be becoming general. Egypt, with the exception of the single stud of Ali Pasha Sherif, possesses no pure blood, nor is it to be found in Tunis Tripoli, or Algeria. In southern Morocco the tradition of pure breeding, if preserved at all, is so only among the remote desert tribes beyond the Atlas – who still boast of possessing strains of blood brought with them in their migrations from Nejd in the thirteenth and fourteenth centuries. Syria is almost stripped of its authentic breeds, once numerous in the Lebanon; and although a considerable sprinkling of pure mares is still to be found in Homs, Hama, and Aleppo, and in the villages of the Euphrates, their quality is far from what it used to be; so much so that the horse-buying commissions sent by the French and other European Governments find it yearly more difficult to acquire stallions of standard merit. In Mesopotamia the breed is becoming more and more mixed, and in all the Bagdad district it has been a byword. A few good mares are still to be found in Persian Arabia but the great studs of the Bakhtiari chiefs are gone, and it is very doubtful whether any pure blood at all is to be found now in Persia proper. Pure Kehailan blood may, therefore, be considered as confined in the present day strictly to Arabia, and even there within ever narrowing limits.

The reasons for this general decline are, first, the ever-increasing military pressure of the Ottoman Government, which has broken the independence of the tribes on the Arabian frontier and limited their areas of summer pasture. Secondly, the gradual adoption of firearms by the Bedouins in their inter-tribal wars, and thirdly, the more systematic 'combing' of the desert for stallions for the Indian market. It has been found that, wherever firearms take the place of the lance, there the tribesmen care less about their horses and revert to their original camel riding in their raids. It is certain too that for many years past the handsomest and strongest colts have been taken away more and more unsparingly from the strength of the breeding stock, while the tribes have contented themselves with less and less perfect stallions for their stud use. The blood has remained the same, but the stock has declined in vigour, in beauty, and in excellence.

The following is a list of all the tribes of whom it can safely be affirmed at the present moment, 1897, that they are possessed of the true Kehailan blood stock:

Sebaa	Shammar
Fedaan	Rowala
Ibn Haddal	Montefik
Anazeh	Oteybeh
Kahtan	Harb (a few)
Muteyr	Beni Suleiman (a few)
Ajman	Daffiri

There are also in Arabia certain studs still flourishing in the hands of princes and individuals which are recognised as authentic. The chief of these are the studs of the Emir Ibn Rashid at Hail, of Eid et Temimi at Oneyzeh, of the Emir Ibn Khalifa at Bahreyn, and of the Sultan of Muscat. Outside Arabia the only Eastern stud of any importance recognised by the Arabs as authentic is that of Ali Pasha Sherif, at Cairo, which is held in great respect by them, as descended from the mares and horses collected, at the expense, it is said, of a million sterling, fifty years ago in Nejd by Abbas I, Viceroy of Egypt. The Ottoman Sultans Stud at Constantinople is of recent growth and of no special value. It is a collection of some 800 stallions, many of them of great beauty, but of which pedigrees have been lost and of some 40 mares, few of them 'mazbutat' (of known pedigree) or of the first quality. In India fine horses abound in the stables of the native princes, especially at Jodhpore, and in the hands of the rich Bombay merchants, but few mares; and I do not know of any Indian stud exclusively managed on the Arabian principles of breeding. The Indian Government in 1893 had 147 Arab stallions in stud use in Bombay and the Northern provinces. These had been purchased at from 1,200 to 2,000 rupees, but the price has since risen. In Europe the oldest Arab studs are those of Prince Sanguscko and Count Joseph Potocki, in Poland, both of high quality, which date from the end of the last century, and of the Branicki family in the Ukraine. Although the pedigrees in these are imperfect from an Arab point of view, they all contain mares of fine Arabian type, especially Prince Sanguscko's, and supply magnificent chargers to the Russian Imperial cavalry. Next to these came the Royal Stud of Wurtemberg and the Austro-Hungarian Imperial Studs at Lipizza and Babolna, at all of which establishments great care has been taken in the acquisition of Kehailan mares as well as horses. In Italy there was in the time of King Victor Emmanuel a truly magnificent stud, containing as it did half of Abbas Pasha's famous collection. But it was unfortunately sold and dispersed at the King's death in 1878; while in France, though Arab stallions are largely used for cross breeding, there is still no pure Kehailan 'haras'. Prussia has quite recently been endowed by the Emperor William with a pure stud at Neustadt; but Spain, Portugal, and the rest of the European States are still unrepresented. In England the first attempt to breed from pure Arabian mares as well as horses was made by Mr. Chaplin in 1875, who sent Captain Upton, an enthusiast on the subject to Aleppo; where with the help of Mr. Skene, H.M. Consul, he purchased some authentic stock. But ill luck attended the venture. The best stallion died, and one or two of the best mares proving barren, the project was shortly after abandoned. It was revived, however, in 1877 by the writer of this monograph on a larger scale and with better results. The Crabbet Park Stud, established in the autumn of that year, now numbers some thirty brood mares of the most authentic strains of blood, the produce of which are sold yearly by auction and realise good prices. The average of all sales during the last fifteen years from the stud stands as high as 110 guineas. It is carried on on strict Arabian principles, and as there is no attempt at increasing the height of the stock, the Kehailan type has been well preserved. It has supplied breeding stallions to nearly every part of the globe including North and South America, South Africa, Australia, India, and even Turkey. The Honourable Miss Dillon's stud at Pudlicote, started in 1884, has won many prizes in open jumping competitions.*

In America Arab breeding was commenced some twenty years ago by Mr. Huntington, and has subsequently been taken up, but on no large scale by others. Several small studs exist in Australia, and Arab stallions and mares have lately been imported by Mr. Cecil Rhodes into South Africa. It may be hoped, therefore, that any falling off there may be in his original home is being compensated to the Kehailan elsewhere.

The total census of the Arabian horse cannot be large. Of quite pure authentic blood there are probably not 2,000 brood mares left in Peninsular Arabia, with perhaps as many more among the northern tribes – 5,000, let us say, the world through, all counted.

The Bedouin system of breeding is one rigid in its principles. The noble tribes divide their mares into three categories. 1. The *Mazbutat* (authentic) mares, of absolutely certain pedigree, their ancestors having been from time immemorial in the tribe. From these alone colts are chosen as stallions for the tribe, all others being sold away as

* The Duke of Bedford, Lord Warwick, Mr. Vidal and Mr. Stephens, M.P. are also breeders of the pure stock.

yearlings. 2. Mares taken from other noble tribes and their descendants. These are often authentic, their pedigree being known. But their colt produce is disqualified, and even one of their own Mazbutat mares, if lost and bred from away from the tribe, remains on her return declassed. 3. Mares of unknown pedigree. These in the best tribes are used for riding only, and are not bred from. They go by the name of *Shimalieh*, Northerners, or Kadisheh, mares of no breed, the Mazbutat mares being sometimes called *Nejdieh*, of Nejd, in distinction, though there is no such thing as a 'Nejd' breed.

All authentic mares claim to be descended from certain original strains of Kehailan blood. The most notable are the Seglawi, Managhi, Abeyan, Hamdani, Dahman, Hadban, Jilfan, Toweysan, Saadan, and Wadnan. The pedigrees are chiefly remembered through the dams, the blood of the sire being taken for granted as always beyond question. These are not written in the desert, but kept by oral tradition. Within the tribe the blood of each mare is of common notoriety and so is not a subject for deception, but strangers need to be on their guard.

The single object for which the Kehailan is bred by the Bedouins is service in their wars. For this the qualities necessary are great powers of endurance, the capacity of making long marches, of 300 or 400 miles, without flagging, an extreme sobriety in the matter of food and drink, and a sufficient turn of speed at the end of the raid to overtake the enemy or elude pursuit. Mere speed over a short distance is not encouraged by any system of racing or trials. The sole practical test is in the raid ('ghazu', Italianised 'Razzia'). What is of at least equal importance with speed, inasmuch as all fighting is done with the lance, is perfect shoulder action, facility in turning, a light mouth, intelligence and courage. All these qualities are conspicuous in the true Kehailan, and seem inherent in his blood. The rigorous conditions of his desert life ensure a certain hardihood of constitution; his feet are of iron. He stands unsheltered night and day; he is hardened against hot sunshine and bitter winds. The Bedouin camp is a perpetual turmoil of noise: he is bold and coolheaded. From his foalhood the children have crawled among his feet in the tents: he has the temper of a lamb. He is made for the vicissitudes of campaigning life, and is thus the most complete light cavalry horse imaginable for all countries where hard work and short commons, especially under a burning sun, are the rule of the campaign.

As a racehorse, the Kehailan, though not scientifically bred for the purpose, would seem to have in him a natural quality of speed superior to any other natural breed. Neither the Tartar of Eastern Asia, nor the Cossack, nor any of the unimproved European breeds, can at all compare with him on this head; and it is only his own illegitimate descendant, the English thoroughbred, that has at length distanced him. For over a hundred years he figured victorious against all comers on the Indian turf, and until quite recently he held his own there even against English blood. Latterly, however, he has become less in fashion in India, and has had to give place on most racecourses to the improved Waler, who, thoroughbred or nearly thoroughbred, has been found able to beat him at an allowance. At the present time Arab racing proper is nearly confined to the Bombay Presidency, where the horses arriving from the Persian Gulf are first landed. Here the general price given for a Kehailan of the best strains is from 1,500 to 2,000 rupees before he has been tried for racing, or 2,500 to 3,000 when tried successfully. In the rest of India, Arabs figure mainly as polo ponies, and are run in races of that class when under the standard height. In the palmy days of Arab racing in India, the performances of the best horses were very nearly on a time level with those of our own thoroughbreds.

On the English turf it is rather as a sire of racehorses than as himself a racehorse that the Kehailan is honoured. Few of the imported Arabs, even of the eighteenth century, distinguished themselves as winners; and in the present century, no pure Kehailan has carried off an important race. The last Eastern horse entered for any of our classic contests was in 1863, when the Duke of Beaufort's Barb 'Mazagan' ran for the Goodwood Cup, high hopes being entertained of him by his owner and trainer; but in the event he was easily beaten. In 1883, through the exertions of Lord Calthorpe, Lord Bradford, Prince Batthyani, Mr. Edward Weatherby and others, the Jockey Club, in the interests of horse breeding, consented to the establishment of a special race for Arabs, to be run at Newmarket yearly at their July meeting; and a single contest took place in accordance with their decision in the following year. Fifteen Arabians were entered and eight of them appeared at the post, including two that had run well on the Indian turf, with the result that Admiral Tryon's 'Asil', a three-year-old colt, bred in England from an Anazeh mare imported in foal from Aleppo, proved the winner. The same colt, however, was shortly afterwards beaten in a match by 'Iambic', an English thoroughbred of inferior class; and this was considered so discouraging that the Arab race has not been renewed. The superiority of the English thoroughbred on the flat cannot indeed be contested. At the same time it is by no means proved that a new infusion of Kehailan blood would not be an advantage to breeders for our turf; and Lord Bradford's experience is encouraging. From Arab mares mated with Bend Or and Chippendale he has had produce in the second and even in the first generation which have proved winners of good English races, notably of the Dee Stakes at Chester, and he is continuing the experiment.

The practical value, however, of the Kehailan lies undoubtedly in his 'role' of sire to half-bred stock, especially for all such countries as suffer from extremes of heat and cold, drought, poverty of pasture and general bad conditions of life. For this purpose he is inestimable, for he has the power of transmitting to his half-bred offspring his own enduring qualities, with much of his speed, action and courage, and no little of his beauty. In this he is superior to any but the very highest class of our English thoroughbreds, and has been successful wherever he has been fairly tried. Certain rules, however, are very necessary to be laid down in the choice of Arabians as stallions, the neglect of which will lead to failure; and, as it is a subject not well understood, I think I cannot do better than close this monograph with a few practical suggestions in the interest of breeders.

The first point in choosing an Arab stallion, as indeed any other, for stud use is to be certain of his blood. Unless the horse chosen can show a clean Kehailan pedigree it will always be a matter of chance whether his stock proves satisfactory. Many a stout horse on the Indian turf has proved a despicable sire, and many an unconsidered slug a good one. Apart, however, from pedigree, and where this cannot be ascertained, there are certain characteristics of shape and figure which very seldom mislead, and a certain ideal type without an approximation to which no Arabian ever yet proved of value as a stock getter. The Arabian points are not very different from those of our English thoroughbred sires of eighty and a hundred years ago; and there are half-a-dozen representations in the collection of *Portraits of Celebrated Race-horses*, which might stand for those of Kehailans of the highest type. Such are 'Flying Childers' (the portrait without saddle), 'Sedbury' 1734, 'Dungannon' 1780, his grandson 'Walton' 1792, his great grandson 'Partizan' 1811, and above all, 'Sultan' 1816, an almost perfect type of the pure Kehailan. 'Actaeon' 1822, and 'Venison' 1833, are the latest that show any strong Arabian character in this collection, all the recent portraits having diverged widely from the type. If the reader wishes to contrast the Arab points with those of the modern thoroughbred, he cannot do better than set the portrait of 'Sultan' side by side with that of the great modern racehorse 'Fisherman'. Of living 'English' sires 'Petrarch' and Bend Or come nearest to the Kehailan type.

The best Arabian sires are about 14 hands 2 inches high, of great thickness through, depth and substance, but very short on the leg and with the shortest possible cannon bones; the feet large, deep and perfectly round; the legs clean and flat, with a fair amount of bone, say $7\frac{1}{2}$ to 8 inches below the knee; powerful forearms and second thighs; broad knees and hocks; but a greater development of bone than 8 inches seldom goes with the highest quality. The horse should cover a deal of ground, but should have a short back, with just sufficient space between the wither and rise of the loins for a short saddle. The wither should be high (this is an original Kehailan characteristic found in no other natural breed), but not exaggerated, and the highest point of the croup should be nearly level with it. It is a great point of breeding that the tail should be set on high and that it should rise at an angle of about 45 degs. from the point of insertion, curving, however, sharply downwards so as just to clear the hocks in walking. It is no defect that the tail should hang a little sideways, that being often the effect of a twist given it at the foal's birth by the Bedouin breeder for luck. Both mane and tail should be fine as silk and fairly abundant, never heavy. The shoulder should be well sloped, but without the exaggeration of the English hunter's. It should have, however, the freest possible action, and there is no better test of quality than to turn a colt loose in a paddock and take note of how he moves his shoulders and forearms. There should be little high knee-action, but the whole limb should be thrown forward and the hoof 'dwell' a second in the air before it is put down. This, with corresponding action behind, like that of a deer trotting through fern, is most important in a sire and a great test of quality. The most characteristic point, however, of all in the Kehailan is his head. It is difficult to describe this intelligibly. It should be very broad between the eyes, the forehead high and slightly convex, but with a sudden upward turn of the profile, such as is seen in the gazelle. This can hardly be too exaggerated. The muzzle should be extremely fine, the lips delicately compressed, the nostrils set somewhat high and on a plane with the face in repose, but capable of great expansion when excited; great depth of the cheek bones and width at the throttle; great distance between the eyes and the ears, the head well set on and the neck arched. The following are the exact measurements of 'Mesaoud', bred by Ali Pasha Sherif, the most successful stallion of the Crabbet Park Stud, also of the head of 'Sherifa', a Nejd mare bred by the Emir Feysul Ibn Saoud, both admirable types.

Measurements of 'Mesaoud' at ten years of age: Height, 14 hands 2 inches; girth, 69 inches; from summit of skull to wither, 38 inches; from wither to root of tail, 47 inches; tail bone, 18 inches; from summit of skull to point of muzzle, $23\frac{3}{4}$ inches; round jowl and forehead, 37 inches; round muzzle, $19\frac{1}{2}$ inches; wither to knee, 45 inches; knee to pastern, $11\frac{1}{2}$ inches; point of hip to point of hock, 40 inches; point of hock to fetlock joint, $17\frac{1}{2}$ inches; round forearm, 19 inches; round cannon bone $7\frac{3}{4}$ inches; round hoof 16 inches; length of ear from junction with skull $5\frac{3}{4}$ inches.

Measurements of the head of 'Sherifa': From the summit of skull to point of muzzle, 24 inches; round jowl and forehead, 36 inches; round muzzle, $14\frac{1}{2}$ inches; width between cheeks $5\frac{1}{2}$ inches.

The best Kehailan colours are: 1. Bay with black points. This would seem to have been the original wild colour, and, is that principally esteemed by the Bedouins, especially a dark full bay with the black markings well above the knees and hocks. 2. Chestnut, a strong bright chestnut with mane and tail of the same shade, accompanied generally with three or four white feet and a blaze. These markings are commoner among the Anazeh tribes than in Nejd. Pale shades of chestnut should be avoided, but a sprinkling of white hair is not a disadvantage. 3. White. This, when quite pure, is perhaps the best as it is the most beautiful of all colours. It is the 'fortunate' colour with Mohammedans, and for this reason has been more carefully bred for than any other. The most perfect Kehailan types I have seen have been white, or in advancing years flea-bitten. No Kehailan, however, is ever foaled white, and for the first five years colts go through many changes of coat, from bay, chestnut or nearly black to rose-roan, iron grey and grey. A white stallion should not be used as sire, says Guarmani, till he attains his full white colour at eight years old. White is the favourite colour in Nejd; and all the great collections have been mainly white, notably Ibn Saoud's at Riad, described by Palgrave, Abbas Pasha's in Egypt, and Ibn Rashid's at Hail. Except in the Sultan's stables at Yildiz, I have never seen a quite black Arabian, and I doubt black being a true Kehailan colour, though Bedouins say it occasionally occurs. Dun, blue roan, and piebald certainly are not. The skin, where clear of hair, especially round the eyes, should be in all cases of a deep slaty blue. The eyes should be large and prominent, and shaped like the human eye, the white showing well round the cornea. This is very characteristic of the pure Kehailan.

The chief modern works to be consulted on the subject are:

Pietremont's *Chevaux Préhistoriques et Historiques.*
Doughty's *Travels in Arabia Deserta.*
Naturalist's Library, Section by Colonel Hamilton Smith.
Upton's *Newmarket and Arabia.*
Lieut.-Colonel Hallen's *Reports to the Indian Government, 1892–3.*
Palgrave, *Travels in Central Arabia.*
Lady Anne Blunt's *Bedouins of the Euphrates.*
Lady Anne's Blunt's *Pilgrimage to Nejd.*
General Tweedie's *Arabian Horse.*
Sidney's *Book of the Horse.*

THE ARABIAN HORSE
by Wilfrid Scawen Blunt

Reprinted from the *Standard Cyclopaedia of Modern Agriculture*. Published by The Gresham Publishing Company in 1907.

Although the position formerly claimed for Arabia as the sole original home of the horse in his wild state has long been abandoned, and although even the extreme antiquity of the horse there as a possession of the Bedouin Arabs has been denied by such high authorities as Hamilton and Pietremont, the balance of scientific opinion in our day seems to be that the Kehailan or Arabian thoroughbred represents, in reality as by tradition a primitive wild horse stock indigenous to the Arabian peninsula. Like the Barb, his fellow progenitor of the English racehorse, the Kehailan would seem to have acquired his special characteristics of speed, sobriety, and endurance, with his fineness of coat and limb, from the long isolation of his kind among desert surroundings – surroundings which have imparted the like qualities of beauty and what we call high breeding to the hare, the fox, and the gazelle, indeed to all desert mammals. These last qualities can hardly have been acquired under domestication, and must, therefore, represent peculiarities inherited from the wild state. But it is not at all necessary to suppose a common ancestry between the two desert horses. The Arabian is probably an offshoot of the Asiatic, the Barb of the European wild stock. They are distinguished from each other by difference of conformation sufficiently marked. Whereas the Barb is what the Arabs call 'ram-headed', that is to say, with a convex profile line, the Arabian has the upturned nostril and slightly concave profile of the gazelle. He has the high wither which makes him pre-eminently a saddle horse; and above all, his tail, instead of being set low and carried meanly between his hocks (the Barb characteristic), springs from the highest level of the quarters and is carried high. These are points of bone structure not to be overlooked, and are important in the Arabian as indications of pure breeding.

The horse of the Bedouin Arabs, though held in immemorial honour among themselves, first came into prominence with the world at large through the great Mohammedan conquests of the 7th and 8th centuries of our era. It was as a warhorse for light cavalry that he was first recognised, one unmatched for endurance in campaigning, especially in arid lands on insufficient food with little water. In this character he overran Western Asia, India, and North Africa, and carried the flag of the Caliphate into Spain and Southern France, the special value of the pure Arabian blood being recognised by a rule of war which assigned one share of the booty acquired to a foot soldier, two shares to a mounted man, and three shares to the rider of a horse of pure Arabian breeding.

High prices seem at all times to have been given for the pure Kehailan blood. Sums are recorded which it is difficult to calculate exactly in our money as having been paid to Bedouins for individual horses by kings and princes in early Caliphat days, which must have been far in excess of those paid for other horses. Later we have testimony to their money value in a long series of notices left us by European travellers and Oriental annalists, among whom may be mentioned Marco Polo (1290), Makrisi (1440), Niebuhr (1762), and among Englishmen, Sir Henry Blunt (1635) and Hamilton (1723). The home trade with India was already well established in Marco Polo's time, and he gives 100 marks as the current price paid at Aden for horses exported thence. Blunt gives as the price of the true desert blood horse at Cairo 1,000 pieces of eight, and Niebuhr says: 'The English in India purchase these Kochlani (Kehailan) at 800 or 1,000 crowns each'. The most important writer of those mentioned is, however, Makrisi, whose account of the horse-racing carried on in the time of the Mameluke sultans of Egypt is most instructive.

It was in the 14th century, under Sultan el Nassr, that horse-racing first took a definite shape at Cairo under rules as to training, weight-carrying, distances, and even, it would seem, betting, not very different from those introduced at Newmarket 300 years later by our Charles II. El Nassr was a contemporary of our Edward III, and during his long reign the sport reached its highest point of development under royal patronage.

Till then the Barb had been in favour with the Mamelukes for their military evolutions, but under El Nassr horse-racing proper became a chief feature of all displays, and the superiority of the Kehailan was at once apparent. Agents from the Sultan visited every province of Arabia, and immense sums were given, as much, Makrisi affirms, as 60,000 and 75,000 drachmas for stallions and 80,000 and 90,000 and in one instance 100,000 drachmas (£3,000) for brood mares of the purest strains of blood. A great breeding stud was formed at Seriakus, the finest probably that the Eastern world has seen, and rivalled only in Egypt by that got together at a cost of half a million sterling fifty years ago during his short reign by Viceroy Abbas II. In both studs everything was managed by Bedouins in accordance with Bedouin ideas of breeding, nor was any expense spared. Egypt, however, is not a land suited by nature to the horse, as it is almost entirely without natural pasture, and with the death of El Nasr, as later with the death of Abbas, his racing stud degenerated and was finally dispersed.

The systematic introduction of the pure Kehailan into Europe dates from the 18th century only. During the previous century, racing had come much into fashion in England, and much Eastern blood had been imported, principally Spanish and Barb, but now for the first time stallions of authentic blood were procured from Aleppo and other towns on the desert edge, with an immediate effect on the quality and speed of the English racehorse. The most famous of these sires, and the best authenticated, was the Darley Arabian of Managhi strain, one of the best breeds of the Anazeh Arabs. This horse was procured for Mr. Darley, a Yorkshire squire, through his brother, who was at the time British Consul at Aleppo. Another almost equally famous, but whose pedigree remains obscure, though he is said to have been a Zilfan, was the Godolphin, and to these two Arab sires, in varying proportions of blood, every horse in the English General Stud Book traces his pedigree. It is impossible to enter into any nice calculation here, but it may be affirmed generally that at least three-fourths of the blood of the modern English thoroughbred is derived from Arabia, and that to the Kehailan he owes the initial quality of speed, which two centuries of selection has developed into the perfected racehorse we now possess.

Such, briefly stated, has been the Arabian in the past. His modern uses are of a different but hardly less important kind. As a sire of racehorses his day is over in Europe, for the English thoroughbred, bred for no other purpose, has so far outstripped him in speed that his own unimproved pace, though greater still than that of any other natural breed, can no longer be of service on the racecourse. Even in India, where he long held his own, he is seen less and less often in competition with the thoroughbred 'Waler' of Australia, which has command of the modern Indian market. As a sire, however, of half-bred stock all the world over, and especially in those countries where the conditions of life are hard, the Kehailan's value is becoming yearly more recognized. It has been found in Australia, South Africa, and all the subtropical regions subject to great variations of temperature, droughts, and scarcity of pasture, that horse stock got by an Arabian stallion will by its superior hardihood of constitution outlive that got by an English thoroughbred, while retaining all the essential features of high breeding, sufficient speed, staying power, and courage. The Arabian has, too, this advantage over the thoroughbred – an admirable temper, which transmits itself to his progeny. This, with great soundness of wind and limb, and comparative immunity from disease, makes him of the utmost value to colonial breeders, and such is now his principal function in the world beyond the seas. In Europe all the great military Powers understand his merits as a stallion for military purposes, and he is found very generally in use in the government studs. In England, almost alone of European countries, his services are little asked for, the reason doubtless being that we breed no horses specially for cavalry purposes. What breeders aim at in England, apart from the Heavy cart breeds and polo ponies, is to produce a weight-carrying hunter or high-actioned hackney for show as much as for use. These may bring a high price, while horses less showy but fit for real hard work are little needed, and it does not pay to breed them. Nevertheless it may be confidently affirmed that out of big-boned mares better hunters will be bred with a first-class Arab than with any but a very exceptional thoroughbred stallion. Such stock will be found to have far more even qualities of courage, temper, and endurance, besides being sounder than the other, with hardly less size. It is, however, essential that the Arab stallion employed should be thoroughly well selected, not only with regard to pedigree but also to the special points of breeding peculiar to his class. It is not one colt in twenty bred in the desert, even of the purest strains of blood, that is considered worthy of being used there as a sire, and the same caution should be practised in selecting a stallion for use in England. The points to be regarded are principally these:

Apart from the general rules of a soundly developed frame and freedom from constitutional defects, what one choosing an Arab sire should look to is the shape and setting on of the head. This, with a proper carriage of the tail, is the best indication of pure breeding, and its absence implies almost always a faulty pedigree. The head should be beautiful, not necessarily small, but fine and clean-cut, with good depth of jowl, breadth between the eyes, and breadth between the cheekbones. These should be clean of flesh, and the eyes large and prominent. It is no sign of temper in the Arab horse that the eyes should show white round the cornea like human eyes, but is a peculiarity of the breed appreciated by the Bedouins. The line of forehead should be rather concave than convex, that is to say there should be a slight prominence between the eyes with a corresponding slight depression beneath them, giving a delicate upward turn to the muzzle, which cannot well be too finely tapered. The saying that an Arab horse should be able to drink out of a coffee cup is hardly an exaggeration. The skin of the muzzle and round the eyes should be dark and bare of hair; the ears small in the stallion and finely cut; the nostrils set higher than with other horses. The proper attachment of the head to the neck is of great importance. However strong the neck, the attachment should be delicately curved. The mane should be light and fine, also a point of breeding. So, too, should be the tail; this should be set on high, springing as nearly as possible from the highest level of the croup and rising higher than any part of it. Such a carriage of the tail is a feature special to the Pure Kehailan, and so of great importance. These points of breeding noted, a good judge of thoroughbred stock will not often go wrong in his choice of an Arab sire. The Arab wither is high, with more of a saddle back than the English thoroughbred commonly shows, the effect of a higher croup and better ribbing up. Also the cannon bone is shorter and the hocks and knees are more strongly developed. But on all other points of shape, what would recommend a thoroughbred stallion to a breeder should also recommend an Arab Stallion. His action should be from the shoulder and not from the knee, and he should bend his hocks like a deer.

The best height for an Arab stallion is from 14·2 to 15 hands, rather less than more, 14·2$\frac{1}{2}$ being perhaps perfection. It is seldom that a horse of this height shows more than 7$\frac{1}{2}$ in. measurement below the knee. More than 7$\frac{3}{4}$ in. generally denotes a coarser strain of blood. The hoofs should be perfectly round but deep and strong, not donkey shaped or narrow. The question of colour has been much debated. There can be little doubt that bay or chestnut was the original wild colour, as there is a clear tendency to reversion to them. The Bedouins themselves prefer bay, which they think the hardest, but chestnut with three white feet (the off fore dark) is perhaps still more preferred, and it is usually in this combination that the handsomest types of Kehailan are seen. White and flea-bitten greys are favourites with the townspeople, who have a tradition that grey was the Prophets special choice, and for this reason care is taken to breed for it; but it is certainly not the original Kehailan colour, as a grey colt is never foaled to two bay or chestnut parents, whereas two grey parents will often produce a bay or a chestnut. Brown is an uncommon colour, black an extremely rare one. It is generally admitted by breeders that the type is more perfectly produced with a chestnut sire than with any other. It is also believed that chestnut is the original, as it is the most constant Kehailan colour. Alone of all the colours two chestnuts will always produce a chestnut.

Finally, a word must be said about the sources from which pure Kehailan blood may at the present day be procured. It is a melancholy fact that in Arabia itself it is becoming yearly more difficult to purchase first-class specimens of the true Arabian breed. For various reasons, which it would be too long here to relate, but principally from the introduction of firearms among the tribes, and the greater facilities given to exportation by steam communication during the last forty years, the breed has declined, and it is hardly any longer possible to obtain stallions of the class needed in the traditional markets. At Aleppo, Damascus, and Bagdad, where thirty years ago, the supply was still abundant, it is rare now to find a stallion worth importing to Europe. Even at Bombay this is the case, and to the extent that latterly the Indian remount department, having at last resolved to establish a pure Arabian stud for military use in Northern India, has found itself obliged, in default of first-class stallions procurable at Bombay, to make its chief purchases in Europe. The Continental government studs are in the same plight and the yearly commissions sent by them at great expense to the Syrian and Mesopotamian deserts have latterly returned almost empty-handed. On the other hand, Studs have been started outside the Arabian peninsula in which pure Kehailan stock is being successfully raised, and with good promise of rescuing this valuable blood from the extinction threatening it in its primitive home. The most important of these are the two great studs in Russian Poland belonging to Count Potocki and Countess Branicka, both dating from nearly a hundred years ago, with a new one on lines of still more authentic breeding, the property of Prince Scherbatoff. Sultan Abdul Hamid has an extensive establishment at Constantinople, which is not, however, accessible to the unofficial purchaser. In Austria and Germany their respective governments are breeders of the pure Kehailan, and studs have been started in Australia and North America. Above all, in England the Crabbet Arabian stud, founded in 1877 by Mr. Wilfrid Blunt in Sussex, has proved successful in producing the Kehailan type in its full purity. The prices there current for breeding stallions have of late years been from 80 to 200 guineas, nearly all given for foreign and colonial exportation.

THE INTRODUCTION OF NEW BLOODLINES
by Miss P. K. Wolf

The development of the Arab in this country (Britain) has, without doubt, been highly successful, and a standard set and maintained to an international requirement. This evolution has not been haphazard. Genetics, heredity, conformation and environment have been carefully studied and analysed, not only to breed perfection, but to breed to a definite type. Even bad hocks, a notorious trait in the Arab of old, are fast disappearing.

Many breeders today do not take the trouble to study genetics, to chart their pedigrees or even compare conformation of the mare with the stallion. Others believe that if the stallion has top-class conformation, studies of other factors are a waste of time. This, however, is a hit and miss affair and will never give consistently good results. If a mating consistently proves successful, and that mating has been chosen purely for conformation, it will be found it is because the genes are of the right origins. Whatever one breeds, animals or plants, a study of genetics is essential if one wishes to avoid costly mistakes. Briefly, genetics is the science which seeks to account for the resemblance and differences exhibited among organisms and characteristics related by descent.

In the breeding of Arabs we are particularly fortunate to have Lady Wentworth's books, for she proved her theories on breeding, and this enables Arab breeders, not themselves wishing to experiment, to be successful with the minimum of costly mistakes. Although we know that Lady Wentworth bred some 'bad' Arabs, it must be remembered that she only wrote of that which she had proved. Lady Yule and Gladys Yule bred according to the *proved* theories of Lady Wentworth, and to this day the successes both here and abroad of their stallion Rissalix (bred by Lady Wentworth and owned by the Yules) has been quite remarkable. This success is because Rissalix carried in his body cells a gene of double strength, and this was imported to all his progeny. Thus he bred pure to his characteristics in all his issue.

Today, in 1960, we hear from Arab breeders that there is too much Rissalix blood, and that our Arabs are crying out for an outcross. This need only be true if the Rissalix blood has degenerated and weedy Arabs result. As long as the line continues to breed the right type of Arab, conforming to all its desired characteristics, then there cannot be too much of it.

Inbreeding, as long as the genes are of the right strength to produce uniformity, can only do good. Sometimes there are recessives in the parent stock which become apparent when in-bred.

This is not an indication that in-breeding is a bad thing; one must expect occasional imperfections. When, therefore, such occur it is of great importance never to use these defective animals for breeding, but to keep the perfect types and continue to inbreed with them to help speed up purities and perfection.

If an outcross were to be used in this process, new impurities would be introduced and this would be a severe check in the process of achieving the desired result.

Inbreeding for inbreeding's sake is not good unless the breeder knows that the mare and stallion have the right characteristics, and the ability to pass these on to their progeny.

Inbreeding, both experimental and accidental, has been carried on with the race horse since its evolution. Today, one of the most notable strains is the inbreeding to Phalaris, which has become quite intensive, yet it still remains stout. Some pedigrees are saturated with this blood without showing any degeneration in the progeny. This is remarkable for two reasons – (a) the life of a thoroughbred is far more nerveracking than that of other breeds as it has to adapt itself when young to noise, tension, excitement and to be handled by many different people (b) it has not got anything like the long lineage and purity of blood of our Arabs, particularly those in the General Stud Book.

Thus, since our Arabs pure lines are proven, inbreeding must be a success and far less costly for the breeders. Indeed, it is far *more* costly to introduce an outcross of imported blood.

The history of the pedigree is unknown; there is no theory to fall back on, and breeders have to experiment for years before finding out if they are breeding on the right lines.

It must not be thought that outcrossing is wrong. Outcrossing can be worth while and even necessary, but the breeder must be aware in studying the pedigrees that the characteristic genes of the mate are those required to be passed on to the progeny. It is not just enough to choose a stallion for one's mare on conformation and movement. The stallion can impart to the progeny faults which lie hidden in his parents. A perfect stallion might well be the only successful offspring of several identical matings of his sire and dam, and this being so he will pass on to his progeny the defects of his parents.

Only those stallions should be chosen that prove consistently that there is uniformity of the desired characteristics in their progeny.

NOTES ON THE GENERAL STUD BOOK

The Jockey Club, 'an association of noblemen and gentlemen' dates from 1751, and has through the years become the supreme authority and governing body of the Turf.

The control of racing exercised by the Club is absolute. The Rules of Racing have been drawn up by the members with such continual additions and alterations as circumstances have demanded, and adherence to them is rigidly enforced, offences against them being visited by fines of various amounts, and penalties which may effectually prevent those by whom they are incurred from running horses; horses may be disqualified from racing under Jockey Club Rules if, for instance, their owners are found guilty of corrupt practices, or if they run at unauthorized meetings; that is to say, meetings not under rules; and men may be warned off Newmarket Heath and other places where the rules are in force, as in fact they are at practically every place where a thoroughbred horse is likely to run.

The affairs of the Club are directed by three Stewards, whose task it is to see that in all respects the Rules of Racing must be observed and obeyed.

Messrs. Weatherby and Sons are the active agents of the Jockey Club, the connection having arisen from the fact that in 1773, a Mr. James Weatherby first published *The Racing Calendar*, which became the official organ of The Jockey Club. Messrs. Weatherby keep what is known as the Registry Office which deals with the ever-growing volume of records, pedigrees, and registrations of thoroughbred stock in infinite detail. No foal can be registered without scrutiny of its recorded pedigree held at the Office, cross-checked with the Service Record dates of both Sire and Dam. The Registry has authority to reject an entry whose papers do not satisfy them; nor will they permit a name to be given if there is another entry with a similar name.

Messrs. Weatherby publish successive volumes of the General Stud Book at intervals and Supplements to the Stud Book, which give the pedigree of every thoroughbred foal born in that period covered by the Stud Book.

'Not in the General Stud Book' is equivalent to 'Not Thoroughbred'.

Acknowledgements

My thanks are due to many people who have, by their generous help made possible the writing of this book. To George Allen and Unwin Ltd for permission to use extracts from Lady Wentworth's *The Authentic Arabian Horse*, and *Thoroughbred Racing Stock*. For sources of information and permission to use copyrights:

The Fitzwilliam Museum, Cambridge; Gladstone E. Moore, Esq.; C. G. Covey, Esq.; The Arabian Horse Foundation Library, Maryland; Dr Valerie Noli; Mrs Judith Forbis; Mrs R. R. Archer; Miss Christabel Draper.

For the photographs which enlighten the text I must thank breeders and owners from many countries for lending valuable pictures from their private collections— and the following photographers:

Alexander Photo on page 198

O. Balanshin of the U.S.S.R. Tersk Stud Farm on pages 170, 171 and 172

Mary Bancroft on pages 149 and 150

Paul M. Bates on page 167

The British Museum on page 19

The Farmer's Weekly of South Africa on page 177

Miss Diane Gillies on page 122

Johnny Johnston on pages 192, 194, 195, 199, 200 and 202

Robert Holder on page 148

Polly J. Knoll on page 197

Ellen Van Leeuwen on pages 152 (lower) and 169

Messrs Miles Bros. on page 76

M. K. Miller on page 203

Photonews on pages 94–100, 103, 105, 106, 107, 108, 111, 112, 114, 166, 173 and 174

Photopress on page 207

Pony Lighthorse Magazine on page 110 (below)

Queensland Department of Agriculture on pages 122 and 124

V. A. Rose Ltd on page 77

W. A. Rouch & Co. on pages 81 and 82

John Scouller on pages 81 (above) and 193

John Warner on page 81

J. Weston on page 110 (above)